G000256857

SHIPS, SUBMARINES AND THE SEA

BRASSEY'S SEA POWER: Naval Vessels,
Weapons Systems and Technology
Series, Volume 2

Brassey's Sea Power:
Naval Vessels, Weapons Systems and Technology Series

General Editor: Dr G. Till, Royal Naval College, Greenwich and Department of
War Studies, King's College, London

This series, consisting of twelve volumes, aims to explore the impact of modern
technology on the size, shape and role of contemporary navies. Using case studies
from around the world it explains the principles of naval operations and the functions
of naval vessels, aircraft and weapons systems. Each volume is written by an
acknowledged expert in a clear, easy-to-understand style and is well illustrated with
photographs and diagrams. The series will be invaluable for naval officers under
training and also will be of great interest to young professionals and naval
enthusiasts.

Other series published by Brassey's

Brassey's Land Warfare: Battlefield Weapons Systems and Technology Series, 12
    Volume Set
General Editor: Colonel R. G. Lee, obe

Brassey's Air Power: Aircraft, Weapons Systems and Technology Series, 12 Volume
    Set
General Editor: Air Vice Marshal R. A. Mason, cb, cbe, ma, raf

For full details of titles in the three series, please contact your local Brassey's/
Pergamon Office

SHIPS, SUBMARINES AND THE SEA

by

Dr P. J. GATES and N. M. LYNN

BRASSEY'S (UK)

(a member of the Maxwell Pergamon Publishing Corporation plc)

LONDON · OXFORD · WASHINGTON · NEW YORK
BEIJING · FRANKFURT · SÃO PAULO · SYDNEY · TOKYO · TORONTO

U.K. (Editorial)	Brassey's (UK) Ltd., 24 Gray's Inn Road, London WC1X 8HR, England
(Orders, all except North America)	Brassey's (UK) Ltd., Headington Hill Hall, Oxford OX3 0BW, England
U.S.A. (Editorial)	Brassey's (US) Inc., 8000 Westpark Drive, Fourth Floor, McLean, Virginia 22102, U.S.A.
(Orders, North America)	Brassey's (US) Inc., Front and Brown Streets, Riverside, New Jersey 08075, USA Tel (toll free): 800 257 5755
PEOPLE'S REPUBLIC OF CHINA	Pergamon Press, Room 4037, Qianmen Hotel, Beijing, People's Republic of China
FEDERAL REPUBLIC OF GERMANY	Pergamon Press GmbH, Hammerweg 6, D-6242 Kronberg, Federal Republic of Germany
BRAZIL	Pergamon Editora Ltda, Rua Eça de Queiros, 346, CEP 04011, Paraiso, São Paulo, Brazil
AUSTRALIA	Brassey's Australia Pty Ltd., P.O. Box 544, Potts Point, N.S.W. 2011, Australia
JAPAN	Pergamon Press, 5th Floor, Matsuoka Central Building, 1-7-1 Nishishinjuku, Shinjuku-ku, Tokyo 160, Japan
CANADA	Pergamon Press Canada Ltd., Suite No. 271, 253 College Street, Toronto, Ontario, Canada M5T 1R5

Copyright © 1990 Brassey's (UK)

All Rights Reserved. No part of this publication may be reproduced, stored in a retrieval system or transmitted in any form or by any means: electronic, electrostatic, magnetic tape, mechanical, photocopying, recording or otherwise, without permission in writing from the publishers.

First edition 1990

Library of Congress Cataloging in Publication Data
Gates, P. J.
Ships, submarines and the sea/by P. J. Gates and
N. M. Lynn.—1st ed.
p.   cm.—(Brassey's sea power)
Bibliography: p.
Includes index.
1. Military oceanography.   2. Submarine boats.
3. Warships–Design and construction.
4. Naval architecture.
I. Lynn, N. M. (Neil M.)   II. Title.   III. Series.
V396.G38   1990   623.8′25′0155146—dc20   89–15906

British Library Cataloguing in Publication Data
Gates, P. J.
Ships, submarines and the sea.
1. Ships design   2. Oceanography
I. Title   II. Lynn, N. M.
623.8′1
ISBN 0–08–034735–5 Hardcover
ISBN 0–08–033626–4 Flexicover

Cover photograph: USS *Catfish* (SS-339) operating off the coast of Hawaii. Courtesy of the US Department of Defense.

Printed in Great Britain by BPCC Wheatons Ltd., Exeter

Contents

Acknowledgements

Grateful acknowledgement is made to the following for material used in this book:

Table 1.1 from Holmes, A. (1978) *Principles of Physical Geology* (Nelson Press). Figures 1.1, 1.2, 1.4, 1.5, 1.6, 1.7, 3.2, 3.16 & 4.14 from The Open University. Figure 1.9 from Stoneley, R. JAPEC (UK). Figures 3.7 , 3.8, 3.10 & 3.11 from McLellan, H. J. (1985) *Elements of Oceanography* (Pergamon Press). Figure 4.1 from Tchernia, P. (1980) *Descriptive Regional Oceanography.* Figure 4.2 from McLellan, H. J. (1985) *Elements of Physical Oceanography* (Pergamon Press). Figures 4.3 & 4.4 from Pickard, G. L. (1979) *Descriptive Physical Oceanography* (Pergamon Press). Figure 4.8 from Beer, T. *Environmental Oceanography* (Pergamon Press). Figure 4.13 from Defant, G. (1961) *Physical Oceanography* (Pergamon Press). Figure 4.15 from Bolin, B. & Stommel, H. (1961) *On the Abyssal Circulation of the World Ocean* (Pergamon Press). Figure 4.16 from Pickard, G. L. (1979) *Descriptive Physical Oceanography* (Pergamon Press). Figure 4.18 from Tchernia, R. (1980) *Descriptive Regional Oceanography* (Pergamon Press). Figures 4.19 & 4.24 from Stommel, H. (1958) *Deep-Sea Research* (Pergamon Press). Figure 4.27 from Pond, S. & Pickard, G. L. (1978) *Introductory Dynamic Oceanography* (Pergamon Press). Figures 4.29 & 4.30 from Defant, G. (1961) *Physical Oceanography* (Pergamon Press). Figure 4.34 from McLellan, H. J. (1985) *Elements of Oceanography* (Pergamon Press). Figure 4.39 from Beer, T. *Environmental Oceanography* (Pergamon Press). Figure 4.40 from Fearnhead, P. G. (1975) Formation of fronts by tidal mixing around the British Isles, *Deep-Sea Research* **22**, No. 5 (Pergamon Press). Figure 4.41 from *Deep-Sea Research* (Pergamon Press). Figures 4.45, 4.48, 4.49, 4.51, 4.53 & 4.55 from Tucker, D. G. & Gazey (1966) *Applied Underwater Acoustics* (Pergamon Press). Figure 4.54 from McLellan, H. J. (1965) *Elements of Physical Oceanography* (Pergamon Press). Figure 4.56 from *Military Electronics/Counter-measures* (1981) (Pergamon Press). Figure 2.2 from Thurman, H. V. (1983) *Essentials of Oceanography* (Charles E. Merrill). Figures 2.8, 3.5, 3.19, 3.21, 3.23, 3.24, 3.30 & 3.31 from Rawson, K. J. & Tupper, E. C. (1968) *Basic Ship Theory* (Longmans). Figure 3.17 from Moskowitz, L. (1964) Estimates of the power spectrum for fully developed seas for wind speeds of 20 to 40 knots, *J. Geophys. Res.*, **69**, No. 24. Figures 3.25 & 3.27 from Kehoe, J. W. Brower, E. N. & K. S. Comstock (1983) Seakeeping and combat system performance – the operator's assessment, *Naval Engineers Journal.* Figure 3.33 from Brackenbury, J. D. (1981) Seakeeping, *Journal of Naval Engineering.* Figure 4.17 adapted from Sverdrup, H. U., Johnson, M. W. & Fleming, R. H. (1942) *The Oceans* (Prentice Hall Inc.). Figures 4.21, 4.22

& 5.12 from Munk, J. W. (1983) Accoustics and Ocean Dynamics, in *Oceanography, The Present and Future*, ed. Brewer, P. (Springer–Verlag). Figure 4.23 from Gross, M. Grant (1988) *Oceanography* (Charles E. Merrill). Figures 4.28 & 4.37 from Harvey, J. G. (1976) *Atmosphere and Oceans: Our Fluid Environment* (Artemis). Figures 4.52 & 4.55 from *Military Electronics/Countermeasures* June 1981. Figure 5.3 Adapted from Gregg, M. C. *The Microstructure of the Oceans*, copyright (1973) by Scientific American, Inc. All Rights Reserved. Figure 5.5 from Natural Environment Research Council, *Remote Sensing of the Oceans*. Figure 5.16 from Haber, G. Solar power from the oceans, *New Scientist*, March 1977. Figure 5.17 from Ingmanson, D. E. & Wallace, W. J. (1979) *Oceanography, An Introduction* (Wadsworth).

Crown Copyright/RN photographs and illustrations are reproduced by permission of the Controller of Her Majesty's Stationery Office.

Preface

From the earliest times, man has exploited the sea as a source of food, as a medium for trade and as a means of extending his power over others. The sea became an area of conflict where interests were protected and power projected. But the sea is alien to man and its ever-changing conditions presented a formidable challenge. Both in peace and in war, the sea was a constant enemy and any lapse in the struggle against the elements quickly led to loss of ship and life.

Today, mineral wealth has added to the potential resources of the sea in the shape both of oil and gas in coastal waters and the minerals of the deep ocean basins. The sea is now used to such an extent that the declining level of natural resources like fish and the increase in pollution are causing concern. Laws and conventions have exemplified a new spirit of co-operation and have helped control pollution in particularly badly affected places like the Mediterranean. Similar co-operation in scientific research has improved the understanding of the air–sea interaction and its effects on the world's weather systems. Balanced against these co-operative endeavours, however, is the emergence of powers intent on establishing control of these offshore assets. As a consequence, the roles of navies have changed, and their number grown.

Technology has increased the complexity of modern naval tasks. It has changed some elements of the marine equation but left others as they were. Although ancient mariners would recognise the navigational problems presented by strong ocean currents or the difficulties of firing weapons from a rolling platform, they would be quite lost by consequences of the new technology like the detection of submarines in deep cold water or the use of radar for missile control in bad weather. All this has intensified the need for a sound understanding of the marine environment and its effect on man's use of the sea.

The mariner must still go down to the sea: to fight, to guard, to trade, to explore, to exploit. The sea itself continues to operate to the same unavoidable rules of wind, wave, current and tide as it always has. A knowledge of how the ocean works and how ships and submarines are designed to cope with the physical and chemical behaviour of the sea is a necessary part of an appreciation of the role of navies and sea power in the modern world.

For this reason, Jonathan Gates (a naval constructor) and Neil Lynn (an ocean-ographer) have co-operated in writing this book about ships, submarines and the marine environment. In Chapter 1 they describe the way in which the world's coastlines, oceans and seas originated. In Chapter 2 they examine the nature of sea water, how it is composed and why; they then show the many ways in which the design and fitting of ships and submarines is intended to cope with the problems set by sea water. In Chapter 3 they concentrate on the sea's surface and on the nature of wind and wave. Ships must be designed to suit this demanding environment and the authors show what the basic principles are.

In Chapter 4 the internal structure of the deep oceans and coastal seas is described and its connections with all types of sea use, both civil and military, are established. In particular, the behaviour of sound in water is given some emphasis. In the last chapter, the book is rounded off by a survey of contemporary research into the marine environment and problems associated with resource extraction and pollution are highlighted.

Opinions expressed in this book are those of the authors and should not be taken necessarily to represent those of any official or private body with which they may be associated. The authors are grateful to John Richards for his help with the illustrations and especially to their respective families for patience and forbearance during this maritime expedition.

GEOFFREY TILL
Series Editor

About the Authors

Jonathan Gates was educated at the University of Kent at Canterbury from which he received BSc and PhD degrees.

In 1974 he joined the Corps of Naval Constructors and held a number of posts in submarine, surface ships and weapons sections. He was the project leader for the concept studies which resulted in the Single Rôle Minehunter. He was then posted on loan to University College, London where he established an MSc Course in Marine Electronic and Electronic Engineering. He is currently employed by SEMA Group Systems Limited where he is managing a number of projects in ship and weapons design.

Dr Gates is a Member of the Institution of Electrical Engineers and of the Royal Institution of Naval Architects. He has published a number of articles in leading naval journals.

Neil Lynn is a Principal Lecturer in the Department of Nuclear Science and Technology at the RN College, Greenwich, a Visiting Lecturer to the City University and a Consultant in Oceanography to the Open University. He leads a team actively involved in research into the pollution of coastal waters and, using space-borne instrumentation, also works on the problem of sediment transport.

Abbreviations

AABW	Antarctic Bottom Water
AACW	Antarctic Circumpolar Water
AAIW	Antarctic Intermediate Water
ABW	Arctic Bottom Waters
ACW	Atlantic Central Water
ASDIC	Allied Submarine Devices Investigation Committee (now called Sonar)
ASW	Anti-submarine Warfare
B	(Symbol) Centre of Buoyancy
CTD	Conductivity/Temperature/Depth (Probe)
DSL	Deep Scattering Layer
CZCS	Coastal Zone Colour Scanner
DSL	Deep Scattering Layer
FRP	Fibre Reinforced Plastic
G	(Symbol) Centre of Gravity
GRP	Glass Reinforced Plastic
GZ	(Symbol) Distance Between Righting Moment Forces
ICW	Indian Common Water
IOC	Intergovernmental Oceanographic Commission
IR	Infra-red
JASIN	Joint Air-Sea Interaction (Experiment)
MW	Mediterranean Water
NABW	North Atlantic Bottom Water
NADW	North Atlantic Deep Water
NDE	Non-Destructive Examination
OTEC	Ocean Thermal Energy Conversion
PCW	Pacific Common Water
RADAR	Radio Direction-finding and Ranging
SAR	Synthetic Aperture Radar
SEASAT	Oceanographic Satellite
SI	Système Internationale (International System of Units)
SOFAR	Sound Fixing and Ranging
SONAR	Sound Navigation and Ranging
SWATH	Small Water-Plane Area Twin Hull (Ships)
T/S	Temperature/Salinity (Diagram)

List of Tables

List of Figures

Chapter 4

Chapter 5

1

The Ocean Basins

Two-thirds of the globe is covered by water; an outside observer might be forgiven if he were to miss the continental masses and think of Earth as a planet of water. Table 1.1, however, shows that water, either in the ocean basins, or the fraction found on land or in the atmosphere, is only 0.02 per cent of the mass of the whole Earth, and that this is spread in a very thin layer over the outer shell of the globe. The average ocean depth is only 0.06 per cent of the total Earth radius; in effect, the planet has a damp skin.

This is in strong contrast with the atmosphere, where activity extends up to 150 kilometres, about 1.6 per cent of the Earth's radius. Despite the great depths of the average ocean basin, oceanic processes are largely two-dimensional; vertical motions are of limited extent, waves, tides and water transport are mainly in horizontal directions. Again, the contrast with the atmosphere is to be noted, where the rise and fall of air masses, coupled with horizontal flow, make up the world's weather systems.

The distribution of heights and depths above and below sea level for the whole globe is shown in the hypsographic curve, Figure 1.1. This curve gives the percent-

TABLE 1.1
Volume, Density, Radius and Mass of the Components of the Earth

Division	Average thickness or radius (km)*	Volume ($\times 10^6$ km^3)	Mean Density (g cm^{-3})†	Mass ($\times 10^{24}$ g)
Atmosphere				0.005
Oceans and Seas	3.8	1,370	1.03	1.41
Ice Sheets and glaciers	1.6	25	0.90	0.023
Continental Crust	35	6,210	2.8	17.39
Oceanic Crust	8	2,660	2.9	7.71
Mantle	2,881	898,000	4.5	4,068
Core	3,473	175,500	10.7	1,881
Whole Earth	6,371	1,083,230	5.517	5,876

*Although *Système International* (SI) units should be used in oceanography, nautical tradition has left a wide variety of non-SI units in general use; as an example, the *knot* (equal to 0.514 m s^{-1}) is still the usual unit for ship speed.
†Amongst the units widely used in this book are: y^{-1} (per year), m^{-3} (per cubic metre), and s^{-1} (per second).

1

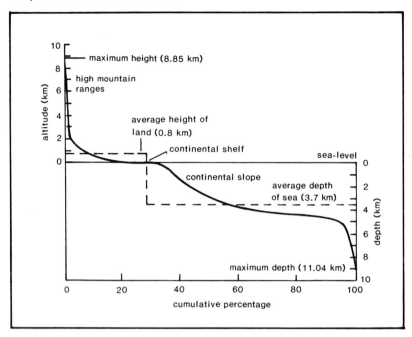

FIG. 1.1   The Hypsographic Curve

ages of the Earth's surface that lie above or below any given level. For instance, 30 per cent of the surface lies at or above sea level and 95 per cent is shallower than five kilometres below the mean sea surface. The average continental height is 0.8 kilometre above sea level, the average ocean depth 3.7 kilometres; the world average is 2.4 kilometres below sea level. Two distinct levels stand out from this curve, the continental platform, between nought to one kilometre above sea level, and the deep ocean floor, between four and five kilometres; and a very small proportion of the continents are very high, with the maximum elevation of 8.85 kilometres. A small fraction of the oceans is very deep, the maximum depth known is the Marianas Trench in the Pacific Ocean at 11.04 kilometres.

Geographically, the World Ocean can be subdivided into three major oceans, the Atlantic, Pacific and Indian. The general data is listed in Table 1.2. The Pacific Ocean is the largest, deepest, and coldest and is surrounded by a volcanically active border, the 'Pacific Ring of Fire'. The Atlantic is the shallowest, warmest and bordered by seismically inactive margins; the Atlantic drains the largest land area relative to its size. The Indian, the smallest of the group of three, is deeper and colder than the Atlantic, and has seismically quiet land masses around it.

TOPOGRAPHY OF THE OCEAN BASINS

The development of the echo sounder led to a systematic examination of the ocean floor following the Second World War. The sea bed was found to be as irregular and

TABLE 1.2

Surface Areas and Drainages of the Major Ocean Basins with Average Depths, Temperatures and Salt Content

(Adjacent seas are included in these figures: the Mediterranean, Black, and Arctic Seas are included in the Atlantic Ocean)

Ocean	Ocean Area	Land Area Drained	Ratio of Ocean Area to Drainage Area	Average Depth	Average Temperature	Salinity*
	($\times 10^6$ km^2)			(m)	(°C)	
Pacific	180	19	11	3,940	3.14	34.60
Atlantic	107	69	1.5	3,310	3.99	34.92
Indian	74	13	5.7	3,840	3.88	34.78

*The salt content of sea water is termed its 'salinity' and is a measure of the total quantity of all the dissolved substances in a sample of sea water. It used to be measured in units of parts per thousand (p.p.t.), symbol ‰, which is equivalent to grammes per kilogram. Modern practice is to use the Practical Salinity Scale. This is dimensionless, but numerically is almost the same as the earlier values quoted in p.p.t.

complicated as the land. The earlier concept of vast areas of flat, deep, and featureless plains spanning the distance between continents gave way to a picture of long sinuous mountain ranges encircling the globe, hidden under the sea surface. Canyons cut the edges of the continents, deep trenches parallel some continents offshore, and the flat plains of the sea bed are dotted with extinct or active submarine volcanoes. Figure 1.2 shows the topography of the sea bed on a line of latitude from the Pacific Ocean, across South America, the South Atlantic Ocean and on to Africa. Figure 1.3 shows the overall picture of the World Ocean floor. The main features are discussed in the following sections.*

The data for Figures 1.2 and 1.3 were obtained from *echo-sounding* studies. A pulse of sound is emitted from a *transducer* beneath the ship, travels downwards, strikes the sea bed and is reflected back to the transducer where the echo is detected. Knowing the velocity of sound in sea water (see Chapter 4) means that one can use the pulse travel-time to calculate the total water depth. This technique, perfected after the Second World War, was a considerable improvement over the old *lead-line* method of earlier centuries, and is now routinely used in all *hydrographic surveying*.

Aboard the *SEASAT* satellite in 1978, a *radar altimeter* was used to measure the surface topography of the sea surface. The enhanced gravitational field over the larger sub-surface mountain ranges, and the reduced gravity above the very deep areas of the oceans causes the sea surface to copy the bottom topography on a smaller scale. Figure 1.2 shows this relief.

*There is a difficulty in drawing profiles of bottom topography for diagrams such as Figure 1.2; horizontal distances across oceans are of the order of thousands of kilometres, while the vertical depths are in kilometres. Therefore, in order to show these bottom features, a considerable exaggeration of the vertical scale is required.

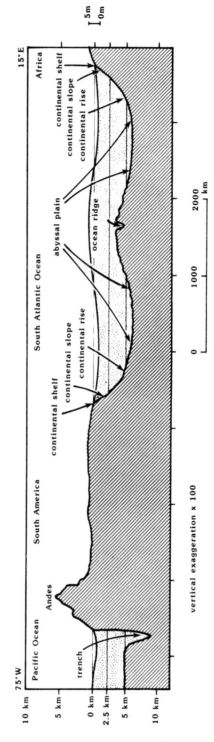

FIG. 1.2   Cross-section of the Earth's Crust from South America to Africa showing the Topography of the Ocean Floor. The topography of the sea surface, from satellite radar measurements, is exaggerated.

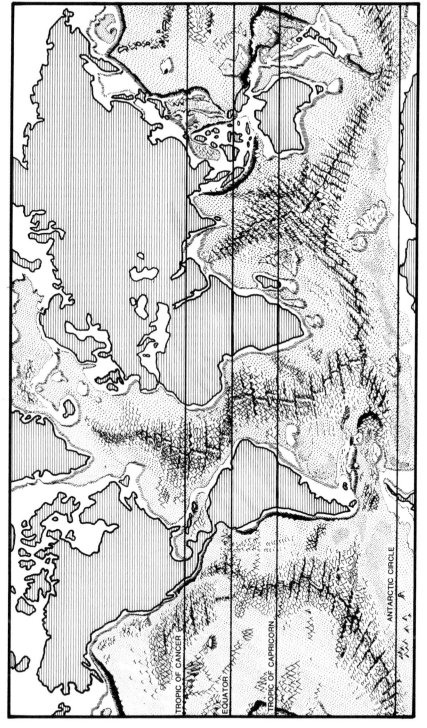

Fig. 1.3   The World Ocean Floor

Abyssal Plains

The deep ocean floor, called the abyssal plains, occupies 42 per cent of the total oceanic area. These flat, usually featureless plains, with gradients of less than one metre in one kilometre, and depths of the order of four to six kilometres, consist of a thick carpet of sediments from a variety of sources. Some originates from continental sources, such as clays, sands and rock debris eroded from the land mass and brought down to the ocean by the rivers. Volcanic dust settles out from the atmosphere into the oceans. Rocks and boulders frozen into the glaciers of the polar regions are rafted out to sea in icebergs; these slowly melt and deposit their load far away from their polar origins. Some clays are derived from the weathering of oceanic rocks themselves, but the majority of the sea bed is covered by the *oozes*, the shells and remains of minute organisms, the *plankton*, which are the microscopic plants and animals of the surface waters.

Low relief features, such as hills, and meandering valleys which resemble rivers, can be found on these plains, related to earlier volcanic activity or sediment transport routes into the deep ocean from the land masses. Sedimentation is a slow process; material accumulates on the bottom at an average rate of one millimetre per thousand years. Despite this, most ocean basins are covered by deposits hundreds of metres thick.

Economically, these plains have been used in the past as a dumping ground for industrial wastes, radioactive substances, toxic gases, munitions and other undesirable items, although international conventions and environmental pressure groups are trying to regulate these activities. The abyssal plains themselves have economic wealth of their own. Especially in the Pacific, strange rocks consisting of manganese and a suite of more economic ores, 'grow' (at a rate thought to be of the order of one millimetre per million years), sitting on the sea bed. Exploitation of these *manganese nodules* cannot be too far in the future, when land-based ores become scarce. Nodules are also found with high phosphate concentrations, valuable as fertiliser, but exploitation of these would have to compete with abundant sources on the continents.

Mid-Ocean Ridge

Down the centre of most of the ocean basins is the Earth's longest mountain chain, known as the *Mid-Ocean Ridge* system. This covers 33 per cent of the ocean area, extends for some 50,000 kilometres, with an average width of 1,000 kilometres, a relief of two kilometres above the abyssal sea floor, and reaching to about 2.5 kilometres below the sea surface. The extent of the chain is best seen in Figure 1.3, looking at the Atlantic Ridge; this shows the numerous fractures known as *transform faults* which cut the ridge transversely, and the *axial rift valley* which is seen to mark the centre line of the ridge, roughly symmetrical on either side of the rift.

These rugged mountains consist of geologically young rocks of volcanic origin, known as *basalts*. They are thrown up at the rift valley and carried sideways by the Earth's interior processes, a system known as *Plate Tectonics*, which will be discussed in the next section. The Atlantic Ocean has the only example of the ridge extending above the sea surface, producing the island of Iceland, although this may be also

FIG. 1.4   The Axial Rift Valley in Iceland (*The Open University*)

related to a *hot spot*, which will be discussed later in the chapter. Many of the small-scale features of the mountains and the axial rift valley can be seen cutting across this island in Figure 1.4. Iceland exhibits the same volcanic heat and lava flows as the rest of the submerged ridge.

In certain rift valleys, the Red Sea for instance, pools of mineral-rich water and sediments have accumulated, 2,000 metres below the sea surface. These are thought to be a product of hot water circulating through the highly-fractured rock of the rift system, leaching out metals from the fresh basalts. These fluids and deposits have very great economic potential, with high concentrations of iron, copper, nickel and zinc. Similar deposits of metalliferous sediments, but without the pools of hot water, have been found in other mid-ocean ridge systems. Here, jets of very hot water, in excess of 300°* have been found squirting out of the ocean floor water laden with minerals leached from the newly-cooled basalts from the *magma chamber* beneath the ridge.

These jets are thought to be the outlet of what is called the *hydrothermal circulation*, where cold sea water is sucked into cracks and fissures of the mountains which flank the rift, heated deep in the crust by the hot rocks and discharged by the jets on to the valley floor. The exchange processes between the hot water and hot rocks do much to maintain the balance of sea water chemistry, as will be discussed in Chapter 2. It is estimated that a volume of water equivalent to the total ocean passes through the hydrothermal system in about five million years. It is now thought likely that the pipework of the circulation system extends out well beyond the rift

*The pressure of the sea at these depths keeps the water from boiling at its atmospheric value of 100° Centigrade.

mountains on either side of the spreading axis. This exposes large areas of rock to the hot sea water, permitting many chemical exchange reactions to take place.

If, by accident of geology, these active mid-ocean rifts die out and their remains are pushed up on to continents by crustal processes, these rock formations are a rich source of valuable ores such as copper, silver, lead and gold. The Troodos Mountains of Cyprus, with their long history of mineral extraction, are such a formation.

Seamounts

Scattered throughout the oceans, usually rising from the abyssal plains are some 10,000 undersea active or inactive volcanoes called *seamounts*. The Pacific Ocean has most of these undersea mountains. Some break the surface as islands, for example the Hawaiian chain, or the Azores; some do not reach the surface, and others, termed *guyots*, have flat tops, submerged to a depth of one to two kilometres, the remains of an island eroded flat by wave action, and now sinking back into the oceanic crust.

Although the pattern of seamounts may appear random, in several places they occur in recognisable straight lines across the ocean. The Hawaiian chain is the best example of this, with the youngest, active volcano in the chain, Mauna Loa to be found at the east, with the chain then extending north and westwards across the Pacific.

Trenches, Continental Rise, Slope and Shelves

Along the landward edge of the oceans, the topography of the ocean floor joins that of the continental land mass across two types of margin, the Atlantic-type or *aseismic margin* or the Pacific type, the *seismic margin*. These margins occupy 21 per cent of the ocean area and geologically can be considered part of the adjacent continent; as such, they can contain the same series of mineral resources as the nearby land. This makes ownership of such areas valuable for surface or sub-surface deposits if the local geology of the shelves is appropriate.

As its name suggests, the first type of margin is seismically inactive, that is there are no volcanoes or earthquakes associated with this zone. For this reason they are sometimes called *passive margins*. Figure 1.5 shows a typical aseismic margin, showing the gradual rise from the abyssal plain depths called the continental rise, the steep section known as the continental slope, the shelf break, commonly at about 130 metres depth, and finally the wide, shallow continental shelf leading up to the shoreline.

These margins, while relatively flat, can be cut by deep valleys, sometimes associated with continental rivers. Known as *submarine canyons*, they act as conduits for sediments eroded from the continents, deposited on the continental shelf, then carried down the canyons on to the abyssal plains. Mud, rock and debris flow down these canyons in episodic events known as turbidity currents, sometimes triggered by earthquake shocks, racing out on to the abyssal deeps at high velocity, before slowing down and depositing their sediment load on to the plains. The abyssal *fans* associated with the Asian rivers, the Indus and Ganges show how these sediments can cover

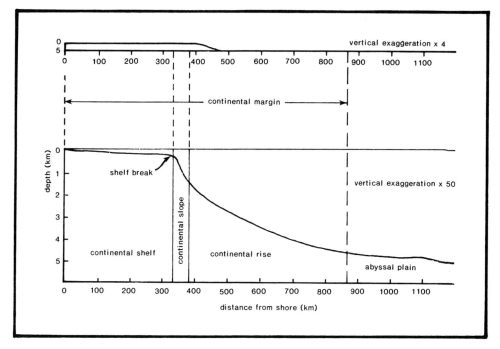

FIG. 1.5   Topography of a Typical Aseismic Continental Margin

large areas of sea floor. Many of these continental margins have entrapped organic remains, which, over many millions of years, have matured to produce oil reservoirs. The continental slopes off Nigeria have such oil deposits.

Figure 1.6 shows the topography of the North European Continental margin, with its series of valleys, spurs and slopes.

The *seismic or active margins*, characterised by the edges of the Pacific Ocean, are geologically active. Japan, Alaska, California and Peru are all well known for volcanic or earthquake activity. These margins can be subdivided into two types.

On the landward side, if there is a continent, such as South America in Figure 1.2, then the result is a mountain range thrown up over the top of the continent, like the Andes in this diagram. A narrow strip of continental shelf separates the trench from the shoreline.

If there is no large land mass, the result is a chain of volcanoes breaking the sea surface, called an *island arc*. The Aleutians in the North Pacific, see Figure 1.3, are a good example of this.

On the seaward side of both of these types of margins there is a deep oceanic *trench*. These trenches, the deepest parts of the ocean, 7.5 to 11.0 kilometres below the sea surface, extend along thousands of kilometres of the continental shoreline. In terms of the World Ocean though, they occupy less than two per cent of the total area.

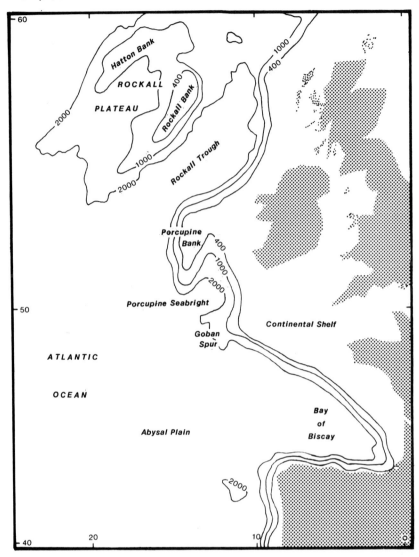

Fig. 1.6   The European Continental Margin, showing the Continental Shelf,
Slope and Rise

The Coastline

The edge of the ocean, the dividing line between the water and the land is dominated by erosion processes. Ocean waves erode the rocks of the land tides and long-shore currents transport the resulting pebbles, sands and muds along the coasts and out to sea. These erosion products join the river-borne sediments brought down from the continents.

Resistant rock formations stand out against this action, forming the rugged headlands and sea cliffs. Less resistant rocks permit the sea to erode the coast and push back the boundary between the land and water. Where there is an excess of material carried by rivers and coastal currents, the land is built out, creating *deltas* and coastal plains.

The detail of the coastline seen today is largely the result of the last period of *glaciation* acting on the rocks of the continents. Twenty-two thousand years ago, the Earth was in the grip of an *ice age*, the Northern Continents were covered with a heavy *ice cap*, much as Greenland has now. The water making up this ice was derived from the ocean; consequently, sea level was a hundred metres lower than the current level. Most of the current continental shelf area was dry, or covered by the ice cap. Rivers had further to fall in their route to the sea, they ran faster, cutting and carrying more material off the land than in present conditions.

In the resulting deep, V-shaped valleys, rivers ran out and across the continental shelves. The Rhine, for instance, joined the Thames in what is now the southern North Sea and flowed westwards along the course of the English Channel to reach the North Atlantic Ocean off the Western Approaches. The glaciers themselves gouged out deep valleys near the coasts.

When the ice age ended, water was returned to the ocean as the ice melted. Six thousand years ago, the sea stood at its current level. The continental shelves and river valleys were flooded by the encroaching sea, the deeper valleys filled with sediments left by the glaciers or by the rivers no longer flowing fast enough to carry the material seawards. The *estuary*, formed from the *drowned river valley*, resulted from this filling up of sediments, while the flooded valleys, cut by the glaciers themselves, became the deep *fjords* or *sea lochs* characteristic of mountainous coastlines such as Norway, western North America or Scotland.

Adjacent Seas

There are a number of adjacent coastal seas on the borders of the major ocean basins. Perhaps 'seas' is a misnomer, because some of these areas, such as the North Sea, are really only extensions of the shallow continental shelf, isolated to some extent from the open ocean. The Yellow Sea, the East China Sea and the Barents Sea come under this classification, as might Hudson Bay and the Beaufort Sea in Northern Canada. The shallow depths, 100 metres to 200 metres, control the circulation of water which is more influenced by tides and river discharge than the behaviour of the adjacent open ocean.

Other seas might be thought of as large embayments in the shoreline of the oceans. The Weddell Sea, the Norwegian and Greenland Seas, the Gulf of Mexico or the Bering Sea for instance, have both large continental shelf areas and deeper regions with reasonably free access for water to the adjoining ocean. These seas play a major role in the formation of distinctive *water masses*, contributing to the world ocean circulation, as will be described in Chapter 4.

Finally, there is the sea which is one in name only. The Mediterranean Sea should really be classed as an ocean. It has all the features described for the major oceans, continental shelves, abyssal plains and remnants of mid-ocean ridges. In fact, as the following discussion on plate tectonics will show, the Mediterranean was at one time part of the single ocean which surrounded a single supercontinent. Splitting and rotation of parts of this original land mass has since closed up the eastern end of the Mediterranean, and almost isolated it from the Atlantic, leaving only a shallow sill restricting the free exchange of water between the two oceans at the Straits of Gibraltar.

The Arctic Ocean is termed the Arctic Mediterranean by some authorities. It too is isolated by a series of shallow sills and does not have free connection with the waters of the North Pacific and North Atlantic at all depths. It has wide continental shelves, covered with sediments scraped off the land during the last period of world-wide glaciation, a mid-ocean ridge which connects with the North Atlantic ridge and abyssal plains on either side. Its circulation and behaviour is dominated by the permanent ice cover, at least two metres thick in summer.

PLATE TECTONICS AND THE FORMATION OF THE OCEAN BASINS

The similarities between the coastlines of Africa and South America have long been noted. It seems as if the two continents could fit together rather like a jigsaw puzzle. The process of wrenching apart a huge continental land mass and moving these two halves sideways, made the idea of *continental drift* a part of science fiction until the pioneering discoveries of Alfred Wegner in the 1920s, which presented compelling evidence for South America once having been joined to Africa as a single land mass. A further discovery was that, in geologic terms, the rocks of the ocean basins as seen today are relatively young, between 100 and 200 million years old,* whereas continental rocks in some locations can be dated to ages 10 times this figure; added to this the discovery of the mid-ocean ridge by echo-sounding, and magnetic evidence from continental rocks, it became apparent that some form of continental movement must have occurred.

When a mechanism for this motion was put forward in the early 1960s, the new science of *plate tectonics* was born; geological theory had to be rewritten. The surface layer of the Earth was found to be divided into a number of rigid blocks, called *lithospheric plates* (lithosphere = solid rock sphere); Figure 1.7 shows the seven large plates and several smaller plates. These plates, which are like thin shells covering the interior of the Earth 'float' over the *asthenosphere* or *weak sphere*, a semi-molten rock which makes up the outer layer of the Earth's *mantle*. Heat from the *core* of the Earth causes the melting of the mantle below the asthenosphere along certain well-defined lines. These lines correspond to the mid-ocean ridge. Molten rock wells up to the Earth's surface at the ridge, solidifying and adding to the edges of the two plates which are consequently pushed sideways. This is illustrated in Figure 1.8, and the mid-ocean ridges are known as *constructive plate margins*. Plates are built up at the rate of 1–2 cm y^{-1} for slow-spreading ridges, the Atlantic Ridge is an example, or 6–8 cm y^{-1} for fast spreading ridges, the East Pacific Rise being the best example of these.

If the early spreading axis ran underneath a continental land mass, then the land would rift apart at the spreading centre axis, both halves moving away from each other, see Figure 1.9, opening an ocean in the gap created. South America broke away from Africa in this fashion some 110 million years ago and the South Atlantic Ocean has widened by 5,000 kilometres since then, an average spreading rate of

---

*Geologists usually abbreviate these dates. '200 million years ago' is written—'200 Ma'.

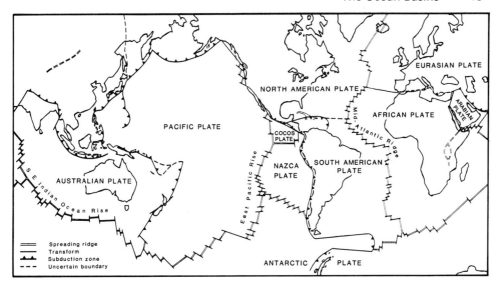

FIG. 1.7   The Major and Minor Crustal Plates of the Earth

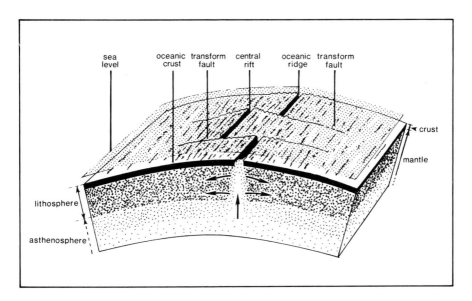

FIG. 1.8   Constructive Plate Margins

$4.6 \, \text{cm} \, \text{y}^{-1}$. The Red Sea, by contrast, broke open 21.5 million years ago, and has drifted apart at a rate of $1.4 \, \text{cm} \, \text{y}^{-1}$.

If plates move sideways away from these spreading centres by building up material at these edges, their far sides must push against other plates further around the globe. At these junctions two results are possible, a *collision boundary* or a *destructive plate margin*. The former is more important to land-based geologists and it occurs when one plate carrying a continent runs into another one. India, travelling northwards

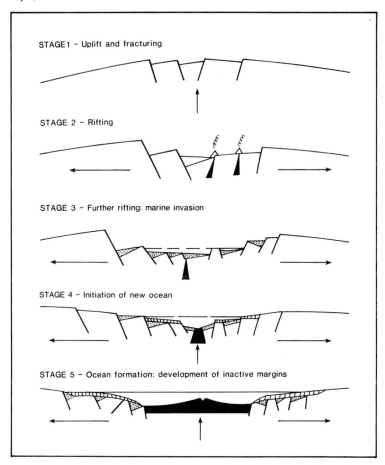

STAGE 1 – Uplift and fracturing

STAGE 2 – Rifting

STAGE 3 – Further rifting: marine invasion

STAGE 4 – Initiation of new ocean

STAGE 5 – Ocean formation: development of inactive margins

FIG. 1.9   The Opening of an Ocean

across the Indian Ocean, colliding with Asia and throwing up the Himalayas at the point of contact, is a good example of this collision boundary. Sometimes the collision results from a rotational motion of a plate; as India moved northwards, Africa rotated clockwise closing the eastern end of the Mediterranean Sea.

When one (or both) of the colliding plates is purely oceanic, that is with no continental land mass on top, we have the margin of most interest to the oceanographer. Figure 1.10 shows the two types of these *destructive plate margins*; the ocean plate on the left is being pushed under the plate to the right. This down-going or *subducted* plate is eventually absorbed back into the mantle, but the frictional forces generates heat at the margin and melts part of both plates; volcanic activity results. This is usually accompanied with extensive earthquake activity which, if the epicentre is near or under the ocean, can generate severe wave activity (popularly known as a 'tidal wave' but more correctly known as a *tsunami*). This will be discussed in Chapter 4.

Early stages of plate destruction yield the *island arcs* referred to earlier, and as time goes on these volcanoes coalesce and large land mass areas are built up. This

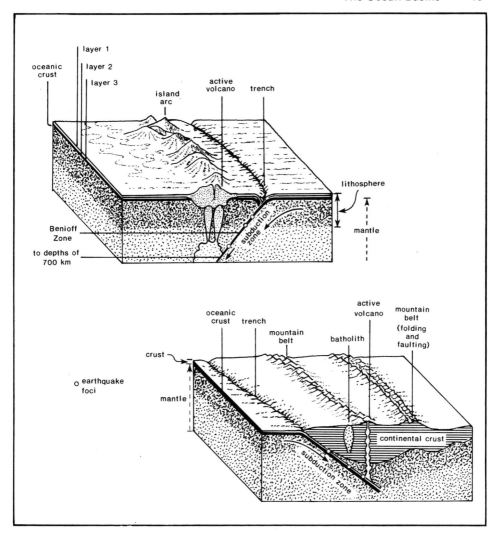

FIG. 1.10   Destructive Plate Margins, Island Arcs and Continental Margins

continental rock is lighter than the rocks of the original oceanic crust and consequently sits on top of the oceanic plate. The early, unrealistic ideas of continents drifting around the globe, ploughing their way across the oceanic floor has given way to the concept of the continents sitting on the lithospheric plates, 'going along for the ride' so-to-speak.

On the seaward side of these destructive margins, the result is always a trench in the ocean floor, where the crust is being dragged downwards as the oceanic plate is subducted under the surface plate.

One feature omitted from this all-encompassing theory of the evolution of the surface of the Earth and the ocean basins is the *seamount* or volcanic island. Although they appear to be randomly distributed throughout the ocean basins, especially the Pacific, some of them can be seen to exist in long chains. The Line

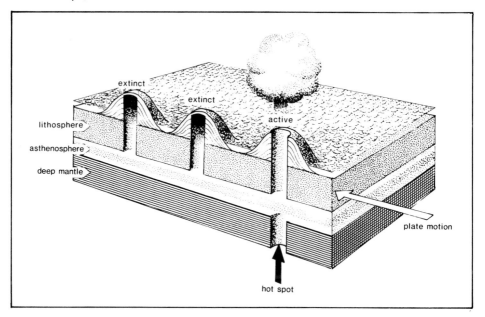

FIG. 1.11   Production of Volcanic Islands at 'Hot Spots'

Islands or the Tuamoto Archipelago form two distinct lines of seamounts and islands. The Hawaiian Islands and Emperor Seamounts form a long line, which has a sharp bend in the middle.

For these features to be created, one imagines a small, concentrated *hot spot* in the mantle, giving off a plume of lava which rises up through the crust and forming the volcanic island. As the oceanic crust moves sideways, so this original volcano is cut off from its source of lava, becomes extinct and starts settling back down into the ocean crust, see Figure 1.11. Meanwhile, at the site of the hot spot, a new volcano is being built up. As the crust advances, so the process is repeated, leaving a trail of seamounts in its wake. The break and sharp turn in the Hawaiian Islands–Emperor Seamount Chain, is thought to have happened when, some 45 million years ago, the Pacific plate changed its direction of travel abruptly from northwards to its current north-westward direction.

CONCLUSIONS

An explosion of knowledge in the last 20 years on the structure and mode of formation of the ocean basins has revolutionised our concepts of the hidden features of the sea bed. The oceans are continually evolving, and although the widening of oceans, at $2\,\mathrm{cm\,y^{-1}}$ or so, is unlikely to have much effect on territorial acquisition and naval planning, it is as well to understand this evolutionary process and that of the structure of the ocean basins.

The distinction between true oceanic sea floor and the continental land mass under the shelf seas can colour a country's view of what territory is under their jurisdiction. Volcanic islands can emerge overnight, and just as quickly disappear. Earthquakes from subduction zones along the coastlines can generate the tsunami, to wreak destruction on foreign coastlines. Finally, the mineral wealth found in some of the mid-ocean ridges, on the deep sea floor, and under the shallow continental shelves, make the geology and evolution of the sea floor a necessary study for hydrographers, coastguards and those tasked with providing a suitable maritime defence for these assets.

2

Sea Water: The Static Problem

The water which fills the ocean basins originated about 3.5×10^9 million years ago from the volcanic gases of the early Earth as it cooled. When the planet's crust was cold enough to allow the water to lie in depressions in the surface and not boil off into the atmosphere again, the oceans were born. It is now necessary to examine the water itself, from the point of view of the oceanographer, and then of the naval architect.

The ship designer has two problems at the start, how to build a ship which floats, and what materials would be most suitable for its construction. Both of these questions are connected to the physics and chemistry of sea water; and in this chapter, the problems of buoyancy and stability in calm waters, and the chemical action of water on the materials of the ship are considered. Although the biology of the oceans is not a direct concern of this volume, marine organisms affect ship's hulls and so these will be considered too.

SEA WATER

Molecular Structure

Sea water is a solution of salts dissolved in water; the majority of the 92 naturally occurring elements, both solids and gases, have been detected in sea water, together with a vast range of compounds, both natural and artificial. The water molecule itself makes this possible; indeed the structure of the water, its ability to dissolve most substances to some degree, and the physical shape of this molecule make the existence of the oceans, and life itself, possible on the Earth.

A water molecule consists of an oxygen atom joined to two hydrogen atoms, the familiar H_2O. These three atoms are bonded together with the hydrogen atoms positioned at an angle of 105°, Figure 2.1; the resulting electron distribution in the molecule leaves the side containing the two hydrogen slightly positive, the other side, with the oxygen atom alone, is slightly negative. This is a *polar* molecule, and it can therefore form weak bonds with other water molecules. These are so-called *hydrogen bonds*. Although about one twentieth the strength of the hydrogen-oxygen bond, they account for water's unique properties. A fluid of similar molecular weight to that of water would melt at $-100°C$ and boil at $-80°C$. Water would be a gas at the

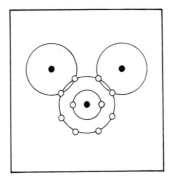

FIG. 2.1   The Water
Molecule

Earth's surface temperature. The polarity of the molecule also accounts for its ability
to dissolve most substances.

Water is one of the few substances on Earth which can exist in three states, solid,
liquid and gas. It is a fortunate accident of planetary evolution that the Earth is at the
right distance from the Sun to allow the majority of water on the Earth to be in the
liquid state. In ice, the solid state, water molecules bond together in a solid crystal
structure, with a density of $0.92 \, g \, cm^{-3}$, Figure 2.2. Despite its open nature, this
structure tends to exclude any dissolved salts and gases and the freezing of sea water
in polar regions results in the ejection of salts from the sea ice.

When thermal energy is supplied to the hydrogen bonds, some of them break
apart, and the ice melts. The resulting liquid water is in fact a pseudocrystalline
substance at ocean temperatures. A loose organisation of clusters of molecules form
and reform rapidly (10^{12} times per second) and water is a mixture of crystals and free
molecules. As the temperature rises, the proportion of free molecules increases until
at 100°C, all the water molecules are free of crystal attachments. Further heating

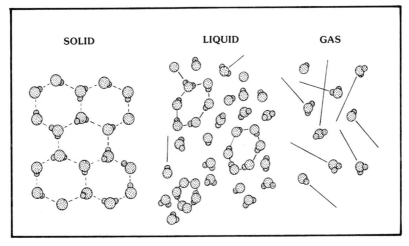

FIG. 2.2   The Crystalline Structure of Water

breaks all the hydrogen bonds and the molecules are set completely free of each other; this is the gaseous state, and the change in the molecular structure in the transition between ice to gas is illustrated in Figure 2.2.

A large amount of heat is needed to break apart the bonds in ice to form liquid water. $2,095\,J\,kg^{-1}$ (joules per kilogram), the *specific latent heat*, is needed to melt ice without raising the temperature. $4,190\,J\,kg^{-1}$ of heat is needed to raise the temperature of liquid water by 1°C, the *specific heat capacity*, and $2,256\,J\,kg^{-1}$ is required to convert water into steam at 100°C, the *specific latent heat of vaporisation*. This is illustrated in Figure 2.3, showing the heat required to change the temperature of water from ice to a gas. These figures are higher than most other substances on Earth and account for the high heat capacity of the ocean. The sea can absorb heat from solar radiation with little temperature change; when sufficient energy is supplied to evaporate the water, very large quantities of heat are released into the atmosphere when the vapour recondenses to fall as rain.

The two working fluids of the planet, water and air, act to redistribute the excess heat of the tropics and the extreme cold of the poles. The Earth stays, more or less, at the same temperature on a yearly average. The high heat capacity also explains why land masses, with a lower specific heat, experience greater swings in temperature by day and night, or season by season. The ocean surface, at any given latitude, experiences a very small diurnal temperature change, of the order of 1–2°C in mid-

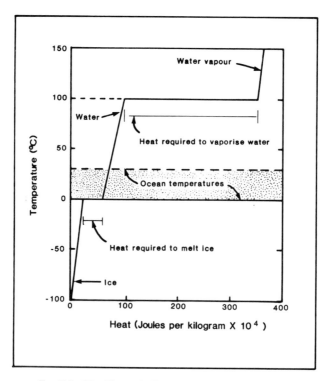

FIG. 2.3   The Change in Water Temperature Following
the Addition of Heat

latitudes, and 5–10°C for seasonal variations. Beneath the surface, temperatures remain very constant, in contrast to atmospheric changes.

Dissolved Substances

In one kilogram of sea water, approximately 35 grammes are dissolved salts or gases. This is usually termed the ocean's *salinity* (see footnote to Table 1.2). Values for salinity vary from 0.1 for river waters entering the ocean, to 34.5–35.0 for 75 per cent of the total ocean water mass.

For the salts, the major elements are chlorine, as the chloride ion, sodium, sulphur, as the sulphate ion (SO_4^{2-}), magnesium, calcium, potassium, and carbon, mainly as the bicarbonate ion (HCO_3-); there are a host of minor constituents. A list of the major elements found in sea water is given in Table 2.1.

These constituents can be divided loosely into the major, minor and trace elements. Some like carbon, phosphorus, nitrogen (as the nitrate ion) and oxygen are linked closely to biological processes; some like calcium and silicon to biological and geochemical processes; others, like sodium, potassium and magnesium react with the rocks of the sea bed. Some take part in few chemical reactions, except as poisons to biological systems, such as mercury and cadmium. All the naturally occurring substances in sea water originate either from volcanic gases which dissolve in the ocean, or by leaching out of continental or oceanic rocks.

TABLE 2.1
Composition of Sea Water of Average Salinity (35)
Major Components

Anions		Cations	
	(g/kg of sea water)		
Chlorine Cl^+	18.9799	Sodium Na^+	10.5561
Sulphate SO_4^{2-}	2.6486	Magnesium Mg^{2+}	1.2720
Bicarbonate HCO_3^-	0.1397	Calcium Ca^{2+}	0.4001
Bromine Br^-	0.0646	Potassium K^+	0.3800
Fluorine F^-	0.0013	Strontium Sr^{2+}	0.0135
Boric acid H_3BO_3	0.0260		

It is the polar structure of the water molecule which can account for the unique ability of water to dissolve most substances. Figure 2.4 shows how water reduces the normal electrical attraction that an atom of sodium has for an atom of chlorine in the familiar compound NaCl—common salt—when salt is dissolved in water; the two atoms now carry single opposite charges and are called *ions*. These attract the oppositely charged ends of the polar water molecule. The ability to dissolve substances also accounts for water's electrical conductivity. Pure water is almost non-conducting, but the addition of any dissolved constituent permits an electrical current to flow, the current being passsed by the ions in solution.

There are small concentrations of dissolved gases in sea water. Wind and wave action at the surface of the ocean saturate the upper layers with the main atmospheric gases nitrogen and oxygen. Phytoplankton, microscopic single-celled organisms, the primary plant life of the sea, also produce oxygen which dissolves in the sunlit upper

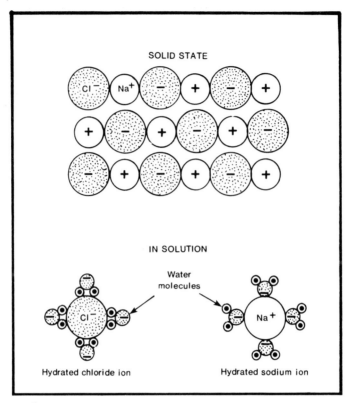

Fig. 2.4   Dissolution of Sodium Chloride (NaCl) in Water

surface layers. The quantity of gas that can be dissolved in sea water is controlled by temperature, the colder the temperature, the more gas that can be taken into solution. For those gases which do not take part in biological reactions, the ocean is nearly saturated at all depths, but for the biologically important gas, oxygen, the distribution with depth is closely linked both with biological production and decay of organic tissue, and with the sinking of cold surface waters.

Density of Sea Water

The density of sea water is controlled by its temperature, salinity and pressure. The first two are the most important, and as the actual measurement of density at sea by a weighing method is almost impossible, the standard technique for determining the density of sea water has always been by a measurement of the water temperature and salt content, then using an internationally agreed formula to calculate the density. Figure 2.5 shows how the density of sea water varies with salt content and temperature over the range of values normally encountered in the oceans.

It can be seen from this diagram that changing the temperature by 5°C, (at a constant salinity of 35) has the same effect as changing the salinity by 0.8 (at a constant temperature of 20°C). Pressure has little effect on density as water is almost

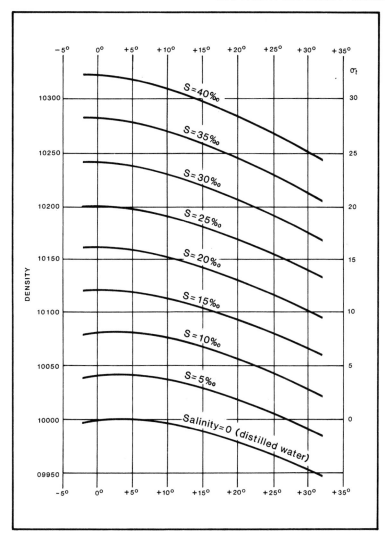

FIG. 2.5   The Density of Sea Water as a Function of Temperature
and Salinity

incompressible and it is only in the very deep oceans that a calculation for water density should include the pressure contribution.

The pressure increases with depth; 10 metres' depth corresponds approximately to one atmosphere in increased pressure. The ocean trenches have pressures of the order of 800–11,000 atmospheres; at this depth, pressures on structures are of the order of 15 tons per square inch (2.3×10^8 Pa).

WATER AS A BUOYANT MEDIUM

When primeval man first set to sea in a canoe or crude raft, he soon discovered the problem of buoyancy, stability, strength and the effects of sea motion on his vessel.

Above all, a ship must float stably, and in this section, the naval architecture of a ship in calm water will be considered.

In designing the size and shape of a ship, a number of factors must be taken into account. First, the hull must have sufficient buoyancy and space for the cargo or equipment it carries. Secondly, the shape of the hull must be such that the weight of the cargo and equipment may be disposed so that the ship is stable (and remains so in rough seas) yet does not present too great a resistance to motion. Chapter 3 addresses the additional considerations which must be taken into account as a result of the effects of waves, which produce ship motion and deck wetness. These waves originate from the interaction of the sea and the atmosphere, which forms the basis of that chapter.

Flotation and Buoyancy—Surface Vessels

Archimedes' Principle states that a body immersed in a liquid experiences an upward force equal to the weight of fluid displaced. In order to float, the volume of the ship below the water must displace a weight of water equal to the total weight of the ship. The upward force produced by the displacement of water is termed *buoyancy* or *displacement*, and is given the symbol 'B'. See Figure 2.6.

As a ship takes on stores, fuel or cargo, it sinks deeper into the water, displacing more water to account for the increased weight of the vessel. As a ship's displacement depends on the weight of these items, it is usual to define the condition of the ship when specifying displacement—light for a vessel without stores, water, fuel and cargo—heavy for a ship when loaded with these items. For comparative purposes, a standard displacement is often used for warships and this is their displacement when

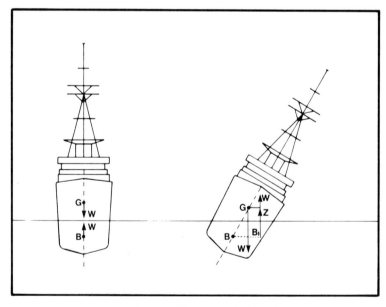

FIG. 2.6   The Buoyancy of a Vessel

fully manned, with stores and ammunition on board, but without their fuel and reserve feed water.

For merchant ships, however, the *tonnage* is often quoted; this should not be confused with displacement (although the latter is often given in units of Tonnes) and it is, in essence, a measure of the internal volume available to carry cargo (the term deriving from the number of tuns, a standard size wine barrel, which a ship could carry). The tonnage is used to calculate port and canal dues. Gross tonnage is generally used for merchant ships; this is the total internal volume expressed in tons of cubic capacity, although *Nett Registered Tonnage* is also used (and is an indication only of that part of the internal volume which can be used for cargo and passengers).

To ensure that a merchant vessel is safely loaded, a *Load Line*, or *Plimsoll Line* showing the level of the waterline at the maximum allowable draught, is marked on the vessel. This mark is determined to ensure sufficient freeboard in sea water at normal summer temperatures. The previous section noted that the density of water, and hence the waterline level, can vary with a change in water temperatures, say from a tropic to polar voyage, or with a change in salinity from oceanic conditions to river passages. Subsidiary draught marks indicate a safe draught in waters of different densities, when with the same embarked cargo, the vessel would displace a different volume (although of course the same weight of water).

In the design of a ship, estimates of all the individual equipment, component parts and structure are an essential prerequisite because, without an estimate of displacement, there can be no meaningful estimate of the size of the vessel. Such estimates can be based on known weights of items, or where they are less exactly defined, (such as the weight of cabling) on scaled data from existing ships. This process is, of course, iterative as the scaling factors may themselves depend on the ultimate result of the

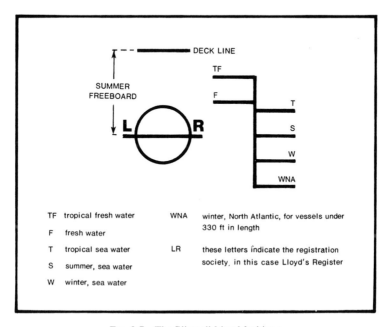

FIG. 2.7   The Plimsoll Line Markings

estimate of displacement (or alternatively, on the size and shape of the hull). Even at the initial stage of the design process, which determines the approximate size, shape and cost of a vessel, there is a process of continued refinement of the estimated parameters, with cross-checks being applied to ensure that the longitudinal and vertical positions of the centre of gravity ('G' in Figure 2.6) result in a design which is stable.

Several systems are used to organise the weight data used in the design process. For warships, most major navies use similar systems; the British system is very similar to that used in America. In each case, the weight of the warship is divided into nine major categories or groups, see Table 2.2. Each of these is further divided into sub-groups which themselves are divided into sub-sub-groups. In each case, the division is limited to nine categories so that each group may be represented by a single digit, each sub-group by two, and each sub-sub-group by three digits. An example of the division of Group 4 into sub-groups is given in Table 2.3 and of Sub-Group 4.3 into sub-sub-groups in Table 2.4.

It is important not only to estimate weight during a ship design but also to consider volume; a classification system, similar to that for weights, is used for volume.

In defining the volume required, deck area is sometimes the critical factor and must be taken into account, especially in the case of electronic equipment. Increasing the deck height, whilst generating more internal volume, creates no more additional useful space for equipment and compensating reductions in deck area cannot be made. *Weather-deck* area is also a factor which requires consideration.

The displacement determines the volume of the hull which will be below the water

TABLE 2.2
Major Weight Categories for Warship Design

Group 1	*Hull*
Group 2	*Propulsion*
Group 3	*Electrical*
Group 4	*Control and Communications*
Group 5	*Auxiliary Systems*
Group 6	*Outfit and Furnishings*
Group 7	*Armament*
Group 8	*Variable Load*
Group 9	*Design and Construction Services*

TABLE 2.3
Division of Group 4 Items into Sub-Groups

Sub-Group 40	*Navigational Systems*
Sub-Group 41	*Internal Communications*
Sub-Group 42	*Ship and Main Machinery Control Systems*
Sub-Group 43	*Weapons Control Systems*
Sub-Group 44	*Ship's Protective Systems*
Sub-Group 45	*External Communication Systems*
Sub-Group 46	*Spare*
Sub-Group 47	*Spare*
Sub-Group 48	*Spare*
Sub-Group 49	*Spare*

TABLE 2.4
Division of Sub-Group 43 into Sub-Sub-Groups

Sub-Sub-Group 430	*Surface/Air Weapon Control Systems*
Sub-Sub-Group 431	*Surface/Surface Weapon Control Systems*
Sub-Sub-Group 432	*Surface/Anti-Submarine Weapon Control Systems*
Sub-Sub-Group 433	*Submerged Launched (Non-Air Flight) Systems*
Sub-Sub-Group 434	*Submerged Launched (Air Flight) Systems*
Sub-Sub-Group 435	*Weapon and Surveillance Radars*
Sub-Sub-Group 436	*Sonars*
Sub-Sub-Group 437	*Centralised Weapon Control Systems*
Sub-Sub-Group 438	*Electronic Warfare Systems (EW)*
Sub-Sub-Group 439	*Spare*

line but there must be sufficient room overall to accommodate all the items which contribute to the weight of the ship. Often, having provided a hull of the appropriate size for weight and stability, there is insufficient volume for all the equipment to be accommodated. The trend to achieve increased performance through the use of electronics with their low density (compared with guns of previous eras), and requirements for associated maintenance and operational spaces, has meant that the hull appropriate for the weight of equipment is often too small. Consequently, modern warship design is generally dominated by considerations of space rather than weight, which was the major factor in previous years.

Two solutions are available—to increase the size of the superstructure, which can lead to problems of stability, discussed in the next section, or alternatively, to increase the length of the ship. Although the latter may pose some structural questions, there are gains to be made both in seakeeping and the reduction of resistance to propulsion.

Intact Stability

Physically, the weight of a ship W, acts as if it were concentrated at a single point, the *centre of gravity*, G, see Figure 2.6. The effect of the water displaced by the vessel is to produce a force equal to its weight (but in an upwards direction) which acts through the centroid of the submerged volume, at a point termed the *centre of buoyancy B*. For equilibrium, both G and B must lie on the same vertical line, and the ship will float in such a way as to ensure that they do. The ship may be heeled over by the application of a moment of force, a *heeling moment*, such as may be produced by wind blowing against the side of the vessel. As the ship heels, part of the vessel which was previously out of the water submerges and part which was formerly submerged now immerses, see Figure 2.6. The position of G is not related to the submerged volume and remains unchanged. The buoyancy force acting through the new centre of buoyancy B will, with the weight of the vessel acting through G, create a *righting moment*. The magnitude of this righting moment is the product of the weight of the vessel and the distance between the weight and buoyancy forces acting in parallel and in opposition. The distance between the forces can be shown by drawing a horizontal line through G. If this line cuts the vertical through B at a point Z, then the separation between the two forces is GZ and the righting moment is $GZ \times W$. If Z is in the direction of heel (GZ is, by convention, taken to be positive in this circumstance), then the ship is stable and will return to the upright if the heeling moment is removed.

If GZ is in the opposite direction to the forces causing the heel (GZ negative), then the ship will be unstable and capsize. Stability thus depends on the movement of the centre of buoyancy relative to the centre of gravity as the ship heels. Figure 2.8 shows the curve of GZ against the angle of heel.

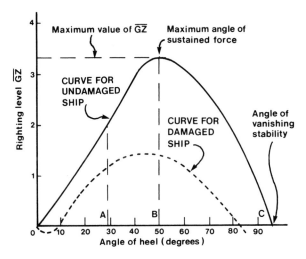

FIG. 2.8   The Curve of GZ Versus Angle of Heel. (—) Curve for Undamaged Ship, (– – –) Curve for Damaged Ship

As the heel angle increases, one side of the ship will immerse further. However the shape of the hull means that the emerging and immersing volumes do not change at the same rate. As a consequence the rate of change of GZ will vary. The largest static, continuous heeling moment that can be applied to the ship without capsize is that which produces the angle of heel resulting in the maximum value of GZ. If a greater moment is applied, the angle of heel will exceed that which produces maximum GZ and, if sustained, this moment will produce capsize. Whilst GZ is positive, however, removal of the moment will allow the vessel to return to the upright position. Once the angle of heel reaches that point where GZ becomes zero, the *angle of vanishing stability*, the ship will capsize and will not return to the upright. Angles of heel between that of maximum GZ and vanishing stability may be experienced dynamically, for instance on rolling as a result of wave action, but the ship will recover so long as GZ is positive provided the heeling moment is intermittent and not a sustained one.

Any fluid in partially full tanks will have a free surface and will run to the low side of the ship as she rolls or heels. Where such conditions exist normally, the GZ curve must be corrected for this unfavourable stability condition. So far only the intact stability under slowly varying conditions has been discussed, but *free surface effects* can have a significant effect on a ship which is damaged and flooded, and on the dynamic response to the wind and waves. This is discussed below.

The techniques which have been described to analyse the *athwartship stability* can also be applied to the longitudinal axis. As may be expected, large moments are needed to tip the ship in the longitudinal plane. The ship tilts about the centre of flotation, which is not necessarily coincident with the centre of buoyancy. Weight added at the centre of flotation will increase the draught uniformly; weight added elsewhere will incline the ship and trim it by the head or by the stern.

Consideration of Stability in Design

The ability of the hull to support the weight and contain the volume of equipment and cargo is the first consideration. To this must be added several other factors, including the margin of stability to allow for the recovery from a heavy roll. The first consideration is to ensure that G and B are vertically aligned in order that the ship floats under normal conditions without heeling.

Stability is influenced by both the shape of the hull (which determines the position B and the form of the GZ curve) and the distribution of the weight of equipment and cargo (which determines the position of G). If much equipment is carried high in the ship, then G will be raised and the stability impaired. It is not the weight alone but the moment produced by equipment which is critical. Thus light equipment carried on a tall mast may be as critical as heavy equipment carried lower down. A heavy radar antenna, which needs to be placed high above the water line for a good radar horizon, can cause stability problems. Large superstructures also cause problems because of the large vertical separation of G and B which this causes. This tends to reduce the maximum value of GZ.

Ships with *flare*, that is with the hull getting broader with height, see Figure 2.9, are less affected by weight increases. Increases in top weight during the design process are often accompanied by increases in the *beam* of the vessel to compensate and maintain the margin of stability. The disadvantage of increasing the beam is, however, that the vessel will achieve a lower speed for the same power or alternatively will require more power to attain the specified top speed. Although the resistance to propulsion can be reduced by increasing the length of the vessel, the larger vessel may have a weight and cost penalty. Longer vessels provide additional volume within the hull and may allow some reduction on superstructure size which may reduce G and in itself reduce the need for increased beam. There is a temptation to provide a large stability margin to allow for poor build estimates during design and growth of the requirements before build. For warships, large stability margins simplify a refit where there is often a requirement to fit heavier weapons or increase the height of the masts. Excessively large stability margins can indeed be obtained from a vessel with a large beam; however, this not only requires greater propulsive power as noted above, but produces poor seakeeping qualities. Righting moment opposes any tendency to roll, and such a ship will roll rapidly, to the discomfort of those on board. Such a platform is also unsuitable as a warship and weapons platform, as in addition to the poor crew performance because of fast roll, the weapons system performance can also be degraded. This degradation will take the form of difficulties of tracking, stabilisation of launchers and antennae, and reduced arcs of fire.

Occasionally, aluminium is used in fabrication of the superstructure, in order to reduce top weight and displacement. The use of aluminium has several disadvanta-

FIG. 2.9   Vessel Showing Pronounced Flare: the Soviet Battlecruiser *Kirov*
(Crown Copyright/RN Photo)

ges which will be discussed in the section on the choice of building materials. As a consequence, it is usual for the penalty of increased cost for a slightly longer vessel, or a reduction in top speed, to be paid for the use of a steel superstructure.

If a ship requires modernisation in which the new weapons or other equipment raise G (which is usually the case) the stability margin is regained by ballasting. This increases the draught of the ship and reduces its speed. In some cases a ship is deliberately constrained to an existing hull form. In these situations, ballasting and other techniques, for instance aluminium superstructures, must be adopted. The provision of a stability margin over and above that required for safety must be balanced against the requirements of speed, seakeeping, and weapons performance. The provision of such usable margins of stability imply a margin in displacement but they must also be accompanied, if they are to be used effectively, by margins in volume and services. These margins must also be correctly disposed if the usable stability margin is to be effectively exploited.

Damage Stability

The previous section has assumed the ship is intact and in calm water. The dynamic response of the vessel is discussed in Chapter 3, but it is worth considering at this point, the effects on stability of flooding due to enemy action, collision or other accident. The results of flooding are loss of buoyancy, loss of both transverse and longitudinal stability and damage to cargo and equipment. These effects are minimised by the provision of a sequence of transverse watertight bulkheads, see

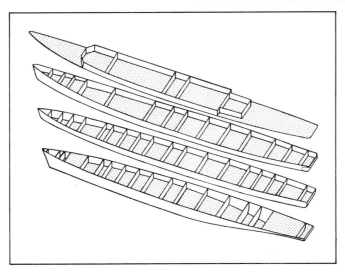

Fig. 2.10   The Watertight Subdivisions of a Frigate

Figure 2.10. These bulkheads extend vertically to the bulkhead deck, often the weather deck for frigates and destroyers. When the vessel sustains the maximum degree of flooding allowed by the reserve of buoyancy it founders; watertight bulkheads avoid its capsize before this degree of flooding occurs. Additional safeguards against extensive flooding are the provision of a collision bulkhead close to the bow, and a watertight double bottom. The space between the double bottom and the hull is often used as additional tankage.

Watertight bulkheads are not only expensive to construct but also incorporate costly doorways and penetrations. In daily use, additional watertight doorways restrict the movement of personnel. A balance must be struck between using a large number of watertight bulkheads (which increases the amount of damage a ship can sustain) and the corresponding penalty of increased cost and inconvenience. Watertight bulkheads have the additional advantage of limiting the spread of fire and smoke. They are good fire boundaries, although fire damage to electrical penetrations of watertight bulkheads can often lead to the loss of watertight integrity in the dangerous situation of both fire and flood.

Flooded compartments can result in the reduction of transverse stability in the same way that the free surface of liquid in tanks affects the undamaged stability. In small ships especially, the results of flooding can be that the righting moment at small angles of heel becomes negative. In this condition, a ship is at its most stable at a few degrees of heel, Figure 2.8. The action of the waves forces the ship to flop alternately between heeling to port and heeling to starboard, an action termed *lolling*. The effects of flooded compartments on transverse stability can be ameliorated to some extent by longitudinal partitions or sills. Longitudinal watertight subdivision is rarely advisable as this could lead to asymmetric transverse flooding and to a severe heel, with the attendant reductions in the reserve of buoyancy. Considerable heel in a damaged condition is not only dangerous from a stability point of view, but does not allow the crew to carry out their duties effectively, or use the armament, which, even if it is capable of effective operation at heel angles beyond about six degrees (which is rarely the case), will have large blind arcs. At high heel angles the use of aircraft and helicopters is also impossible.

The effects of heel, and to a lesser extent, that of poor trim, can sometimes be corrected by the transfer of tanked liquids. As this is a slow process, it may be preferable to counter-flood compartments, especially in the case of large ships which can heel heavily when flooded. For this purpose, large warships are fitted with wing compartments which can be readily filled if counter-flooding should prove necessary. Whilst improving stability, counter-flooding is not without its disadvantages as reserve buoyancy, freeboard, speed and manoeuvrability are all reduced.

Although ships are more stable in the longitudinal direction, this stability can be rapidly diminished by flooding, especially where this occurs at the bow or stern. Once trim is lost, to the extent of deck immersion at the bow or stern, small additional flooding can result in complete loss of longitudinal stability, and the ship will plunge and be lost completely.

The calculation of damage stability must take into account the loss of buoyancy which results from the flooding of a portion of the ship, which is equivalent to the gain in weight due to the flood water. To ensure that adequate reserve buoyancy is present and that the water will not reach the bulkhead deck (statutes allow the water to come only within 76 millimetres of the bulkhead deck), ships are designed to a specified floodable length so that, were this length of ship to be flooded, centred on any point, then the ship will not sink. The calculations assume that there is no permanent heel or list. Ships are specified as to one, two or three compartment standards. A one compartment ship could not survive the flooding of more than one compartment, whereas a only within 76 millimetres of the bulkhead deck), ships are designed to a specified three compartment ship can survive the flood of any three compartments. Warships are specified to a three compartment standard.

Submarine Buoyancy and Stability

The design of a submarine differs from that of a surface vessel as regards buoyancy and stability. Essentially, a submarine has to sink, or remain neutrally buoyant below the sea surface. Indeed, too much buoyancy at the sea surface impedes the rapid submergence of the submarine when required operationally. Weight and weight distribution are of crucial concern to the submarine designer.

The stability of a submerged submarine differs fundamentally as well, from that of its surface counterpart. The stability of the surface ship resulted from a change in the position of its centre of buoyancy as it heeled; as a submarine is heeled however, the relative position of its centre of buoyancy remains unaltered. Stability is obtained by ensuring that the centre of gravity is *below* the centre of buoyancy. In general, this is not too difficult to achieve because the centre of gravity is lowered by the heavy bank of batteries fitted close to the keel; the centre of buoyancy is approximately at the centre of the submarine because of the symmetry of its shape.

As a submarine surfaces, it undergoes a transition from the buoyancy conditions of a submerged body to those of a surface ship, and the design must take this into account. Because of the streamlined shape of the modern submarine which is very efficient underwater, they are difficult to design with good surface stability. However, the advent of nuclear propulsion has eliminated the need for submarines to operate at the surface; the role of the submarine now keeps it underwater for most of its deployment and poorer surface stability can be accepted.

Flotation and Buoyancy—Submarines

A major consideration in the design of submarines is that of pressure. As has already been explained, the water pressure at 10 metres is about double atmospheric pressure. The pressure increases by an amount approximately equivalent to that at the surface for every further 10 metres that the submarine dives. The men within the submarine must be protected from the immense external pressures which water produces at depth. The main part of the submarine is thus a strong central pressure hull, the inside of which is maintained at atmospheric pressure. The pressure hull is surrounded by a casing which encloses tanks external to the main hull. A possible shape for the pressure hull, and the one which can most readily withstand the stresses imposed, is a sphere. This shape is commonly adopted for the research vessels designed to reach the greatest depths, which are called bathyspheres. However, for a submarine, a compromise must be reached between a shape which allows deep diving and one which is easily propelled through the water. The compromise generally employed is a cylinder with hemispherical ends. The cylinder is strengthened by hoop like frames; these are usually inside the cylinder, as a submarine with frames around the outside of the hull is more easily detected by enemy sonars. As mentioned earlier, one consequence of the cylindrical shape necessary for a deep diving submarine is the poor stability that the submarine has when it is on the surface.

Water pressure increases with depth and at a certain pressure, equivalent to the depth which is termed the 'deep diving depth', the hull begins to deform. Accidental excursions to greater depths cause the hull to suffer from fatigue and lose strength from deformation. Such events are recorded, as it may be necessary to reduce the submarine's deep diving depth for subsequent operations. If a submarine dives well beyond its deep diving depth, it could reach its 'collapse depth', where the hull is crushed by the water pressure and from which there is no recovery. The collapse depth is determined by the design and material of the hull.

In order to accommodate missile tubes some submarines have larger diameter cylinders in their central sections. The penalties of departing from the basic cylinder or using large diameter cylinders are principally in the increase in hull thickness and weight required—penalties which are increasingly severe as increases in deep diving depth are sought. The giant Russian *Typhoon* class submarine is believed to be constructed of two cylinders side by side in order to combine a large size with the lightness of the smaller cylinders.

A potential source of failure of the submarine hull is pipework connected directly to the sea water, such as those pipes carrying cooling water for machinery. Each penetration of the hull must be limited in diameter so that, if the pipe to which it is connected fails, then the submarine can recover from the resulting flood. This would be done by blowing compressed air into external ballast tanks, an operation which becomes less effective the deeper the submarine dives. Where large diameter penetrations are unavoidable they must be protected by heavy high-pressure valves which can be used to isolate burst pipes before too much water is taken on board. As deeper diving submarines are designed, an increasing number of the smaller pipes must be protected in this way.

Between the pressure hull and the casing are a number of items which can survive the pressure and can be carried externally. In this space are also the ballast tanks which are used to alter the buoyancy of the submarine as it dives and resurfaces. When the submarine is on the surface, the ballast tanks are full of air. The total weight of the submarine is less than the weight of water it displaces and consequently it floats. When diving, vents on top of the tanks are opened and water fills the tanks through free-flooding holes underneath them. This additional weight of water makes the submarine heavier than the water it displaces so that it sinks. When it reaches the required depth, its descent can be halted by pumping water out of a compensating tank within the pressure hull. When the submarine wishes to resurface the ballast tanks are 'blown' (filled with compressed air).

The compensating tank is used to maintain neutral buoyancy—ensuring that the total weight of the submarine equals that of the water it displaces by varying the amount of water within the hull. This is not an easy control problem since if the submarine sinks its buoyancy is reduced and it sinks more rapidly. It becomes less buoyant because the hull is compressed as it sinks and decreases in volume, an effect which is principally due to the compression of acoustic cladding of the submarine. This cladding, used to make detection by enemy sonars more difficult, is in the form of thick rubber tiles fixed to the outside of the submarine. Neutral buoyancy must be maintained to an accuracy of about 0.05 per cent. The compensating tank compensates for changes in the density of the surrounding water (because of variations in salinity, temperature and, marginally, depth) and changes in the submarine weight because of the discharge of weapons (such as torpedoes or missiles) or the discharge of waste. The size of the compensating tank fitted depends on the range of water densities which the submarine is expected to experience.

It is not only necessary to maintain the submarine approximately neutrally buoyant but also to keep it level (maintain trim). It is particularly important for a submarine to maintain depth and trim when it is 'in the hover'—travelling slowly in order to fire its weapons—or when it is using its periscope. The water at periscope depth, just beneath the surface, can be very turbulent, compounding the problem. The balance of weights which ensure it is level can be upset by movement of personnel, transfer of fuel, or the discharge of weapons. Trim tanks fore and aft are connected by a pipe and transfer of liquid from one tank to the other ensures the submarine maintains trim.

Depth keeping and trim control are also affected by the submarine's control surfaces, or hydroplanes. These are short, wing-like projections from the hull or, in the case of American submarines from the fin, which can be tilted to change the attitude of the submarine. As they act in a similar way to wings on an aeroplane, they are only effective when the submarine is moving through the water. The faster the submarine moves, the more effective the hydroplanes. As a consequence, there are operational limitations on the angle to which the hydroplanes can be tilted which depend on depth and speed. The object of these limitations is to ensure that, in the event of a hydroplane jamming in its tilted position, the submarine could recover before it reached the collapse depth. Hydroplanes are used to assist in diving and surfacing. If a submarine travelling on the surface is venting its ballast tanks in order to dive, then tilting the stern hydroplanes upwards will tilt the submarine bow down. This will enable it to dive more easily. So effective is this manoeuvre that there was a period when some submarines dived with positive buoyancy in case of emergency. That is to say, without the control surfaces, the submarine would naturally float and return to the surface. With the advent of larger submarines, this practice ceased.

THE SEA WATER ELECTROCHEMICAL ENVIRONMENT

Shipbuilding Materials

Traditionally, ships were built of wood; easily available, easily worked and, with proper attention, ships built of wood lasted for decades. Damp rot and wood boring animals, like the *teredo* worm, eventually make replacement necessary. Wood is still used for the construction of some modern warships. In the case of minehunters, for example, the non-magnetic qualities of wood are a distinct advantage. Wood can also be used for small coastal craft and ships' boats, but this role has largely been taken over by glass reinforced plastic (glass-fibre) construction, which has totally revolutionised the recreational boat-building industry.

For the larger vessel there are a number of characteristics which must be considered when choosing materials but in most cases the choice is dominated by building costs and convenience. For this reason, steel is the most popular material for naval construction as it is cheap, readily available and can be cut, shaped and joined easily. Its major disadvantage is that it corrodes rapidly when in contact with sea water and air unless it is protected. The only other metal commonly used is aluminium which, because it has a lower density than steel, is sometimes used for the superstructure, although the overall advantages of this are contentious.

Recently, mine counter-measures vessels, whose magnetic signature requirements can only be met by eliminating all unnecessary metal, have been made from Glass Reinforced Plastic (GRP). The largest GRP ship is the Royal Navy's *Brecon* Class warship with a displacement of about 600 tonnes. GRP is manufactured by impregnating fibres of glass, usually in the form of woven mats, with a plastic such as polyester resin.

Table 2.5 shows the characteristics of the major materials used in warship construction. The grade of steel has to be selected carefully. Some alloys are susceptible to breaking apart under normal loads by a mechanism known as *brittle fracture* at cold, polar temperatures. Oil rigs and Liberty Ships used outside their steel's temperature range have been lost in the past by this mode of failure.

A steel ship or a submarine is constructed from a large number of plates, each cut and formed to the correct size and shape and welded together. Because of the complex shape of the ship this shaping process sometimes involves plates being bent in two directions especially for those close to the bow and stern of the ship. Frames and stiffeners also require cutting and bending to the correct shape. Steel is particularly amenable to these operations. Cutting is performed by melting a thin strip of metal with a high temperature flame, a process often carried out by large automated burning machines. After cutting, the plates are bent, if necessary, by rolling the steel between two small, lower rollers and a slightly larger upper roller. The rotation of the rollers and the downward force exerted by the upper roller are provided by hydraulic actuators.

TABLE 2.5
Properties of Warship Materials

Material	Density kg m^{-3}	Young's Modulus* GPa	Shear Modulus* GPa	Tensile Strength† MPa	Shear Strength† MPa
Steel 50D	7,800	207	80	390	225
Steel HY80	7,800	207	80	617	365
Aluminium	2,800	69	26	150–250	75–150
GRP	<2,000	15–25	4–6	200–300	100–130

*Young's Modulus is a measure of the elasticity of the material under longitudinal forces, stretching or compression, and the Shear Modulus is a measure of the elastic properties of the material under transverse loads such as twisting.
†The Tensile Strength is a measure of the maximum load the material can support when being stretched, while Shear Strength measures the maximum load under transverse forces.

The joining of the steel by welding uses the heat produced by an electric arc between an electrode and the steel which is connected to the earth terminal of the welding equipment. A narrow band of metal on either side of the join, and the tip of the electrode, melt in the extremely high temperatures produced by the electric arc. The molten metal is allowed to cool rapidly, solidifying so that the plates on either side of the join are continuous. The area of the metal which has been affected by the heat of the welding process can be a problem when the ship enters service, if the correct welding procedures are not observed. Flaws and small cracks can form in the heat affected zone and can be a source of weakness and enhanced corrosion. The bending and welding processes can introduce stresses in a surface ship's hull which can cause slight movement when the ship is subjected to the irregular forces of the waves (referred to as 'working').

In submarines, the extreme pressures which they endure mean that not only is the strongest steel used in their construction but that welds are carefully checked for defects. This non-destructive examination (NDE) is also used on important welds in the hulls of surface ships. X-ray or Gamma-ray radiography, for example, is used to produce a three-dimensional photographic image of the weld which can indicate internal flaws not revealed by surface examination. Alternatively, the transmission of ultrasonic vibrations can be used to detect internal faults which could jeopardise the ship or a submarine diving to its design pressure.

Materials other than steel are often suggested for the superstructure of surface ships. The hull in rough weather is structurally similar to beam where the points of support and the loads on it are constantly changing because of the position of the waves. The superstructure can contribute to the strength of the vessel if it is of steel and is rigidly attached to the hull, although there are potential structural problems if the superstructure does not extend to the sides of the ship. If an aluminium superstructure is used it too can be rigidly attached to the hull by welding the aluminium to the steel using an explosive bonded strip method, but this is an extremely costly process. The alternative is to connect the two metals with an expansion joint which not only allows for the different thermal properties of the two metals but also prevents electrical contact, thus discouraging corrosion. Whether the superstructure is designed to contribute to the strength of the ship or not, flexing of the ship in a sea-way can produce cracking in the aluminium. The expansion joint can reduce the stress levels close to the joint but, where the aluminium contributes to the strength of the ship, there is a tendency for any cracking to spread to the main hull structure.

The motivation to save superstructure weight is not well founded as, in general, the size of the hull can be increased slightly to accommodate a heavier steel superstructure without increasing the through life cost of the ship. Fabrication costs of aluminium are about double those of steel because welding must be carried out in an atmosphere of inert gas such as high-purity argon. Recent experience has also highlighted the inferior properties of aluminium when compared to steel under action conditions because it provides poorer ballistic protection and fire containment properties.

GRP has also been proposed as a superstructure material because it is even lighter than aluminium and is sufficiently flexible to avoid stress concentrations which would produce hull cracking. Currently, its cost is comparable to that of aluminium because of the labour intensive nature of the process and the special conditions required to produce effective curing of the resin and to reduce the concentration of toxic fumes to a safe level. GRP is superior to aluminium in the prevention of the spread of fire (because it burns only slowly and has a poor conductivity) and retains its strength under conditions which would cause aluminium to soften. The ability of GRP to contain fragmentation damage is also better than aluminium, which produces secondary fragments. If GRP does not provide sufficient protection then special high tensile fibres may be substituted for the glass fibres. Although these fibres can cost up to 15 times as much as the glass fibres the resulting Fibre Reinforced Plastic (FRP) is an excellent armour-like material. Because GRP and FRP are non-metallic, careful consideration must be given to screening equipment within compartments made of these materials from electromagnetic interference. Despite this shortcoming, GRP could provide an alternative to steel which, although more expensive initially, may prove cheaper through the ship's life because of the lower maintenance costs.

All metals used in ship construction, however, are susceptible to marine corrosion, which forms the subject of the next section.

General Marine Corrosion

The naval architect has one further problem to tackle, linked to the chemistry of sea water, when specifying the material for construction of the vessel. Sea water is extremely corrosive; normally the ocean is slightly alkaline but the high concentration of salts makes it an effective electrical conductor and this enables it to act as an electrolyte in the electrochemical process which results in the destruction of metals, particularly steel, by the formation of their oxides. This chemical reaction is exacerbated by the presence of chloride ions and dissolved oxygen; as noted on page 21, chloride is a major constituent of the dissolved elements and oxygen is usually in a supersaturated solution in the surface layers of the ocean.

Corrosion occurs not only in the submerged parts of the hull, but also in the upper parts and superstructure, as these are almost continually covered by a film of salt water. This film is caused either by sea spray, or from water absorbed from the atmosphere by the hydroscopic salts deposited by the salt-laden spray. The corrosion of marine installations and ships is of great economic importance, with damage estimated in the hundreds of millions of pounds yearly for the United Kingdom alone.

The electrochemical processes which result in corrosion are chemical reactions which occur at the metal surface. They arise because of inhomogeneities which are present in all metals—grain structures of different orientations, inclusions and faults. These inhomogeneities differ in electrochemical potential, and because they are connected electrically, some areas will act as *cathodes* with a surplus of electrons from the metal, and some as *anodes* with an electron deficit. If a portion of the surface with anode-like properties is in contact with an electrolyte, such as sea water, then a chemical reaction can occur which allows the metal to pass into solution as a positive ion. The reactions for steel (or iron) and aluminium are represented as a chemical equation like this:

$$Fe \rightarrow Fe^{2+} + 2e^-$$

$$Al \rightarrow Al^{3+} + 3e^-$$

At other, cathodic areas, compensating reactions occur to maintain electric neutrality, such as those producing the hydroxyl ion (OH^-):

$$O_2 + 2H_2O + 4e^- \rightarrow 4OH^-$$

This is illustrated in Figure 2.11.

In the case of steel, in general terms, the iron and hydroxyl ions tend to combine to

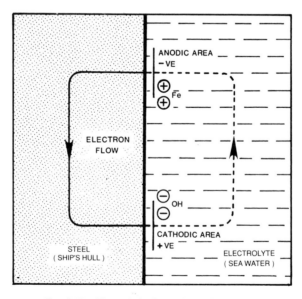

FIG. 2.11   Electrolytic Corrosion in Sea Water

precipitate from solution as the oxidised, hydrated product ferric oxide, the well known red rust:

$$4Fe^{2+} + 8OH^- + O_2 \rightarrow 2Fe_2O_3.H_2O + 2H_2O$$

This is deposited away from the areas of greatest anodic or cathodic activity and consequently the corrosion is not inhibited by corrosion products.

In the case of aluminium similar processes occur, but, unlike steel, the oxide tends to form directly on the surface and produces a protective film which inhibits further action. Alloys resistive to corrosion, such as Stainless Steel, owe their passive nature to such films. With no passive film, Stainless Steel, in its 'active' form, is only slightly less anodic than steel. The oxide film formed renders it passive and effectively extremely cathodic, being even more cathodic than bronze, a traditional material for use as a corrosion resistant material at sea. The significance of the oxide film on Stainless Steel is that it is both mechanically and chemically extremely resilient.

Enhanced Corrosion Mechanisms

Metals that are immersed can suffer very localised corrosion or pitting, even if they are normally resistant to corrosion in moist atmospheres (for instance Stainless Steels). This mechanism arises from local discontinuities which allow the passive film to break down locally and prevent it from reforming, even on Stainless Steels. A similar effect is produced in Mild Steel where some millscale remains, but such corrosion is more akin to that produced by dissimilar metals discussed later. For ships, pitting is more important in the hull than the superstructure, as its mechanism is based on total immersion.

Corrosion can be enhanced by oxygen depletion, which occurs within a crevice. This *crevice corrosion* can be extended to cover any corrosion which occurs as a result of the shielding of an area of the metal by fouling or corrosion products. The mechanism is unclear, but is likely to result from the difference in aeration within and outside a crevice, combined with an increase of acidity caused by migration of chloride ions. Crevice corrosion is a problem both on the hull and in the superstructure. Crevices are extremely difficult to clean or remove during maintenance and remain a constant source of corrosion throughout the ship's life.

A further mechanism for corrosion occurs at grain boundaries in some metals. Though not generally active, areas of Stainless Steel which have been subject to heat, such as near welds, may become susceptible to corrosion because of precipitation of one of the alloy components at the grain boundary. High strength aluminium alloys are also susceptible to the same corrosion mechanisms.

Bimetallic (Galvanic) Corrosion

The corrosion mechanisms described so far have been the result of different properties applying at different areas of the same metal. An extreme, but analogous situation occurs when two metals are connected electrically, such as when they are bolted or welded together. One metal becomes the anode and is dissolved or corroded; the other becomes the cathode and is unaffected. Metals can be placed in

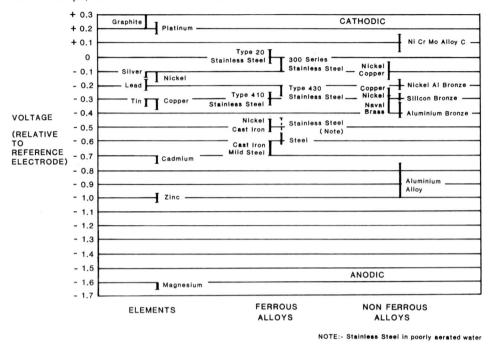

FIG. 2.12   The Galvanic Series in Sea Water

an electrochemical series, see Figure 2.12. The connection of two metals in the presence of an electrolyte results in the corrosion of the more anodic (less noble) of the metals. Thus when brass and steel are connected, it is the steel which corrodes. On the other hand, when steel and aluminium are connected together, it is the aluminium which corrodes. The relative size of the two metals is important—if the anode is very much larger than the cathode, then there may be very little corrosion. If the reverse is true though, then extensive and rapid corrosion results. Cathodic protection, described later, may dramatically reduce the rate of corrosion as bimetallic corrosion is important with submerged hull fittings, although it should not be ignored as a significant source of superstructure corrosion.

Stray Current Effect

Corrosion can be caused by stray currents from the ship's power system. Warships are generally designed, for operational reasons, with power supplies which are 'floating', that is, they are not earthed to the ship's hull. With this type of system if there is an earth fault in one phase of the supply, there is no disconnection or disruption to the supply unless and until a fault occurs in a second phase. However, under the conditions of a single phase fault, currents may flow in the hull. These cause corrosion if the current can find an alternative path through sea water, where this is in contact with the hull owing to small gaps or scratches in the protective paint. These 'holidays' in the coating aggravate the corrosion as the current is necessarily concentrated at these points and can cause significant local corrosion. If the hull takes large currents due to inadequate earthing, during welding operations for instance, this increases the problem.

Rates of Corrosion

Steel in almost static water corrodes at about 125 μm (1.25×10^{-4} m) each year, although the rate decreases with time to half this value after 16 years. If the sea water is moving, as in the case of ships or structures in tidal waters, the rate of corrosion is greater and increases with the relative speed of water over the metal, rising to a maximum of about one millimetre per year at relative velocities of 6 m s^{-1} (12 knots). Temperature also affects the rate and corrosion increases by 20 to 30 per cent for each rise of ten degrees Celsius. Corrosion increases where there is a plentiful supply of oxygen and such conditions apply in the *splash* zone close to the surface of the water. Structures just above the normal sea level have a plentiful supply of oxygen from the air and are continually wetted; those just below the surface are in contact with sea water saturated with dissolved oxygen.

Although corrosion generally requires the presence of oxygen, there is an exception. This is corrosion fostered by micro-organisms which flourish under heavy accumulations of marine growth and corrosion products. These bacteria, which encourage a corrosion based on a sulphate to sulphide chemical reaction, only survive in anaerobic (oxygen-free) conditions.

The presence of calcium, magnesium and strontium in sea water is beneficial as they reduce the rate of corrosion by the formation of calcareous protective films of high electrical resistance at the cathodic surfaces. These passive films act in a similar way to the passive films found in resistive metals.

Results of Corrosion

Generally, corrosion in the short term is merely unsightly. If allowed to persist however, it leads to loss of strength because of the reduced thickness of metal. It can result in the 'binding' of machinery—for instance the failure of a missile launcher because of accretions of rust on the launcher track, causing the missile to stick. Bolts which seize up are a well-known problem arising from corrosion.

Copper alloys suffer from a form of corrosion termed dezincification in which, effectively, zinc is leached from the alloy, causing loss of strength.

A further mechanism which contributes to loss of strength and failure of components arises under conditions in which the metal is under stress. Failures resulting from such stress corrosion cracking are similar to brittle fractures.

Earthing braids or screening braids of cables may, if exposed, suffer from crevice corrosion and rapidly deteriorate. Even the use of Stainless Steel cannot prevent corrosion as pitting and ultimately tunnelling within the confines of the metal, can cause failure. The loss of earthing or ineffective screening can cause particular problems with electronic equipment.

Within the individual items of electronic equipment, even small amounts of corrosion can cause serious problems. Deliquescent corrosion products of aluminium or copper can produce shorting, or result in signal loss due to tracking, where signals jump across printed circuit boards.

The oxide films themselves, which prevent excessive corrosion of aluminium and Stainless Steel, can produce unwanted interference to communications, especially when, as is common, it is associated with poor earthing. Such interference is attributed to the 'rusty bolt effect' and arises from non-linear electrical junctions between metals and their oxide corrosion products. These junctions are similar in form and effect to the non-linear junctions in transistor semi-conductors. The effect takes its name from the junction resulting from the thin layer of rust trapped between a rusty steel bolt and the plates it is retaining. The effect, however, is not confined to bolts and there are several potential sources in the superstructure, such as guard rails passing through stanchions. When such non-linear junctions are illuminated by electromagnetic waves from radar or communications transmissions, a small amount of energy is re-radiated at a different frequency. The non-linear junctions re-radiate both harmonics of the impinging transmissions, and, if more than one frequency is present, a large number of intermodulation products. The frequencies used for communications reception and transmission are necessarily separate and although only a small proportion of the transmitted energy may be re-radiated at a receiving frequency, its magnitude may cause severe interference in the sensitive communications receivers designed to detect very small powers.

Protection from Corrosion

Superstructures and upperworks may be protected from corrosion by good design and painting. Crevices which may encourage crevice corrosion, and bimetallic contacts should be avoided. Painting is the main method by which water is prevented from coming into contact with metal, but when paint cannot be used, *galvanising*— coating with zinc—affords protection as the zinc is preferentially corroded.

Hulls are highly susceptible to corrosion and their paint is difficult to maintain. As they are continually immersed they can, however, be additionally protected by a system of cathodic protection which extends protection to any areas not covered by paint. This method, see Figure 2.13, prevents corrosion by reversing the voltage which drives galvanic corrosion. If the correct voltage is applied to steel for instance, all parts of the metal, whether anodic or cathodic previously, are made cathodic. In order to protect unpainted steel, a current density of $150\,\text{mA m}^{-2}$ is required initially, although this demand falls as calcareous coatings supplement the protection. The current density required by painted steel is about two orders of magnitude less, as most of the area is covered with paint, and the required current can either be supplied by the sacrificial anode technique, to be described in the next section, or by the Impressed Cathodic Protection system described above.

Sacrificial Anodes

The sacrificial anode is similar in principle to the galvanising of steel, but as the hull is continually immersed, a complete covering is not required; local anodes are all that is necessary. Sacrificial anodes may be fabricated from any metal which is more anodic than the steel of the hull; the most common material used is pure zinc, although magnesium or aluminium alloys are also used. Sacrificial anodes have the advantage in that they are simple to install (and cannot be installed incorrectly in a way which would promote corrosion) and require no power supply. In order to maintain the voltage difference, however, a large current density may be required and this necessitates large anodes. For instance, in order to provide $740\,A\,hr^{-1}$ (amps per hour), one kilogram of zinc is required. Sacrificial anodes also require heavy leads in order to keep resistance losses low. Essentially, in sacrificial anode systems, the anode and the protected metal form an electrochemical cell are similar to those in a battery, in order to provide the protective current. As such, it may be considered an expensive way in which to provide this current.

Zinc is the most efficient metal for a sacrificial anode. In sea water, 95 per cent of the current generated by a zinc anode contributes to the protection of the hull. The remainder of the current flows in local circulating currents within the anode. One can go too far though; over-protection can lead to alkaline attack which damages organic paints and to the production of hydrogen. This latter effect can cause embrittlement of steel and lead to the danger of gas accumulation and explosion in confined spaces where cathodic protection is used internally, for instance, in the bilges. With zinc, there is little danger of over-protection but this can happen with magnesium or aluminium alloys, as they operate at potentials more negative than zinc. The zinc of the sacrificial anode must be of very high purity; iron in particular must be reduced to extremely low levels. The other disadvantage of using zinc is that it provides a lower cathodic current and is dissolved at a greater rate than the alternatives. (The rate of dissolution is $20\,mm\,y^{-1}$ when operating at maximum currents.)

Impressed Current Protection

The best defence against corrosion is that of *Impressed Current Protection*, see Figure 2.14. This technique supplies all the electrical current required to give optimum protection under all conditions, provided that sufficient voltage is available

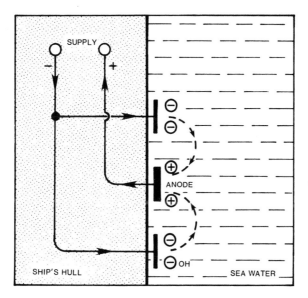

FIG. 2.13   Impressed Cathodic Protection System

and the anode remains functional. The anodes used are far smaller than the sacrificial variety, and the connecting leads need not be large, since the losses may be compensated by increases in the impressed current. Such systems are, however, complex and costly to purchase and install; if care is not taken, they can be connected incorrectly and actually cause corrosion. The systems require a direct current power supply with a high availability and supervision by trained operators.

The voltage applied to the hull is determined in relation to a reference electrode of Silver/Silver Chloride. The normal electrical potential of the hull is, on average, 0.6 volt more negative than the reference electrode. By making the hull about 0.2 volt more negative (that is −0.8 volt in relation to the reference electrode) it becomes totally cathodic. At this voltage difference, adequate hull protection is achieved and the current density of the protective electrical system can be adjusted to maintain this voltage. If failure of the system results in the hull potential exceeding 0.3 volt more negative than normal, then overprotection and hydrogen gassing will ensue.

The anodes used in surface ships of the Royal Navy are of lead in a fibreglass moulding and in submarines, of Platinised Titanium. A typical warship installation is shown in Figure 2.14, with the output controlled by the amplified difference between the hull and the reference electrode voltages; the power is provided by a transformer rectifier unit supplied by the main supply system.

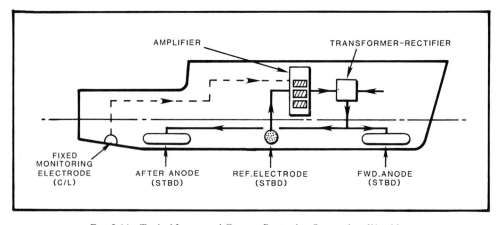

FIG. 2.14   Typical Impressed Current Protection System in a Warship

Marine Fouling

As well as the host of dissolved chemicals in sea water, thousands of species of marine organisms live in the ocean, ranging in size from the microscopic bacteria to the largest mammals, the whales. The bottom living creatures and plants, such as the sea weeds and the barnacle, have an affinity for ship's hulls. This gives the familiar problem of abundant growth on all sub-surface plates which can severely restrict the speed of the vessel; the drag can decrease speeds by 20 per cent for the same applied power. The problem is worse for those areas of the hull just beneath the water line, where higher levels of sunlight aid the growth of plant life.

Figure 2.15 shows an oceanographic instrument for measuring currents after three

FIG. 2.15   Marine Fouling on a Current Meter after Three Months Immersion in Coastal Waters. The
original colour was white (see Fig. 5.4) (*NBA Controls Ltd.*)

months immersion in coastal waters. Barnacles, squirts, sea weed, algae and even crabs were covering the exterior and the instrument had ceased to function correctly.

To stop this fouling and to inhibit the wood boring worm, *Teredo navilis*, the early solution was to sheath the underside of the wooden hulls with lead; in 1761 these were replaced by copper sheets. The copper acted as a poison and cut down on the growth of weeds and barnacles but early trials suffered from galvanic corrosion between the copper and the iron securing bolts until these were replaced by copper fixings. None of these early attempts was completely successful and ships had to be beached and scrubbed down at frequent intervals if their sailing qualities were to be maintained.

The modern solution for metal, or indeed any hull material, is to cover the undersides with a paint known as *anti-fouling*. There are a large number of these compounds available, paints which slowly leach out formulations of copper, tin or mercury into the water for periods of a year or so. Some are very efficient and long-lasting, but their very toxicity to marine life makes them hazardous to persons applying the paint. The compromise is to accept a lower toxicity and repaint (and re-scrub!) more frequently. Indeed, the dangers of anti-fouling paint to the general marine environment are being questioned by some environmental authorities and vessels using some compounds have been banned from these authorities' coasts and harbours.

Recently, however, a group of anti-fouling paints called *co-polymers* have been introduced. The surface layer of these paints dissolves slowly and continuously, releasing biocides. The co-polymer lasts several years and the continual renewal of the surface helps reduce fouling because adherence of the marine organisms is more difficult, and ensures a smooth surface. The anti-fouling and smoothing properties both contribute to reducing the propulsive resistance and fuel consumption of the vessel.

CONCLUSIONS

Sea water is a complex, corrosive mixture of water and dissolved chemicals. The naval architect has to keep a vessel afloat on such a solution, and to stop the ship becoming part of these dissolved salts.

3

The Dynamic Sea Surface

The most noticeable effect experienced in a ship is the motion of confused rolling and pitching when the vessel is under way in a rough sea-way. Even when the weather is calm, swell often produces a gentle movement. These motions result from wind-waves on the surface of the sea. The interaction of the winds on the ocean surface, the dynamic response of the ship, equipment and crew and the efforts of the naval architect to ameliorate these motions form the basis for this chapter.

ATMOSPHERIC CIRCULATION

More solar radiation is absorbed in the equatorial regions of the Earth than at the poles. The extra thickness of atmosphere at the poles due to the tilt of the Earth, see Figure 3.1, and the high reflectivity of the snow-covered polar regions both reduce the energy absorbed at the poles. The equatorial regions, however, do not get hotter, nor do the poles get colder. A transfer of the excess heat from the tropics to the poles smooths out the surplus; the transfer takes place by the ocean currents, with the high heat capacity of water noted previously, and the movement of the atmospheric winds.

Heat absorbed in the tropics causes the air mass to rise, cool, lose water vapour as rain in the equatorial zone and then descend in the subtropical regions. Compression

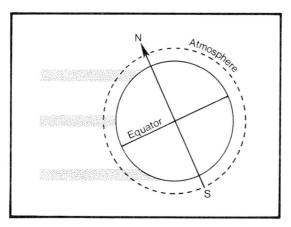

Fig. 3.1   Differential Heating of the Earth by
Solar Radiation

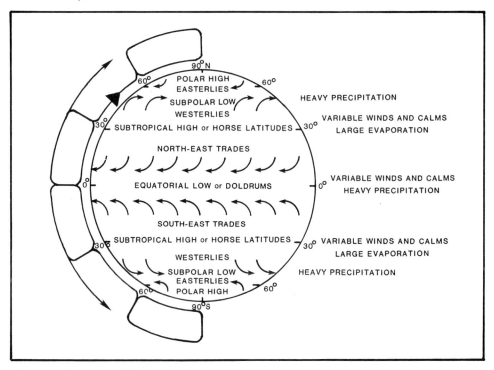

FIG. 3.2   Generalised Circulation of the Atmosphere in Response to Solar Heating, Showing the
Resulting Surface Winds

on sinking warms this air again, and it spreads polewards and back to the equatorial
regions. The poleward air picks up heat and water vapour again from the oceans and
land masses, rises again in the low pressure zone at 60° latitudes north and south of
the equator, to cool and descend on the poles. This complex vertical motion, known
as the *Hadley convection cell system*, is illustrated in Figure 3.2; the implication for
the surface wind, which is of most concern here, is that the rotation of the Earth
causes the surface winds to be deflected and to travel predominantly around the
globe (this is the *Coriolis Effect* which will be discussed in Chapter 4), rather than in a
direct north/south direction as might be anticipated from looking at the convection
cells in the atmosphere shown in Figure 3.2.

The general form of the wind patterns varies with the seasons as the regions which
receive most heat from the Sun varies; the whole climatic pattern moves south to
reach 5°S during January and February then north to 5°N during July and August.
Although the winds follow this movement, the effect of land masses, which heat up
and cool down more quickly than the seas, distort the general wind directions to
produce a much more complex arrangement than that shown in Figure 3.2. The
average system for winter and summer is shown in Figures 3.3 and 3.4.

The general trend of climatic winds is further complicated on a short term basis by
perturbations, especially where the polar and equatorial air patterns meet between
latitudes 30° and 60°. Such perturbations are less common in the Southern Hemisphere, where there is less land to influence them, but north of the equator, local

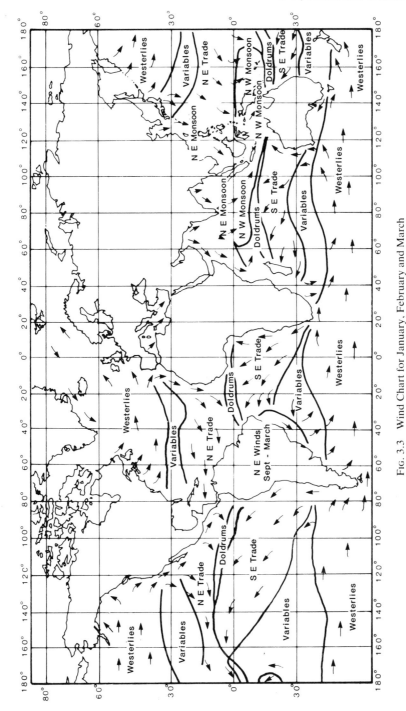

Fig. 3.3 Wind Chart for January, February and March

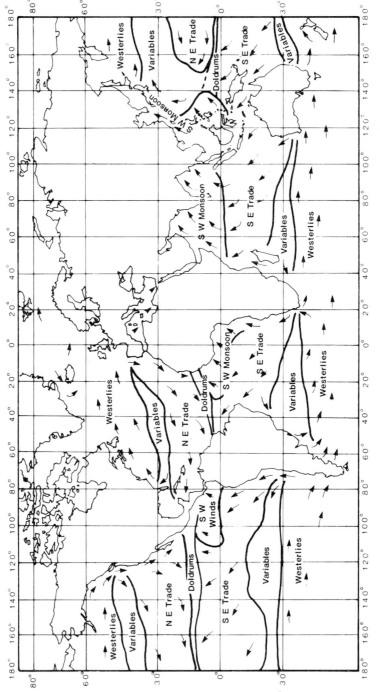

Fig. 3.4   Wind Chart for May, June and July

areas of high pressure, *anticyclones*, form in the eastern Atlantic and Pacific Oceans, and areas of low pressure, *depressions* or cyclones, form in the areas off Iceland and the Aleutian Islands. These result in large changes of wind direction and strength in the Westerlies of the Northern Hemisphere. The areas of local pressure differences are also responsible for much of the precipitation forming at sea in these latitudes. This occurs along *atmospheric fronts*, where warm and cold air meet.

Other regions are not without local effects which may result in stronger or weaker winds than the climatic averages—tropical storms bred in the *Doldrums*, the seasonal *Monsoons* of the Indian Ocean where the whole wind direction changes from the North-East Trade winds of the winter, to the South-West Monsoons of the summer, and the typhoons, tornadoes and hurricanes of the middle latitudes.

Wind Strength

Oceanic winds can vary in strength from the flat calms and light gentle breezes of the Doldrums, through the brisk to strong winds of the Trades and Westerlies, to the hurricane force winds of the violent storms. Although modern instrumentation has superseded older methods of reporting wind strengths, the *Beaufort Scale*, introduced by Admiral Beaufort early in the last century, still remains in general usage despite originally relating wind strength to the abilities of a sailing vessel to cope with the wind. Winds are classified into forces from zero (flat calm) up to 12 (hurricane force winds). These classifications, see Table 3.1, have been more accurately defined in terms of wind speeds. Force 3, a gentle breeze, encompasses the band from 3.4 to $5.4 \, \text{m s}^{-1}$ for instance.

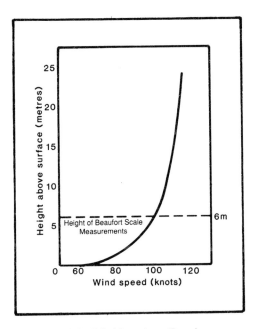

FIG. 3.5   Wind Speed as a Function
of Height above the Sea Surface

TABLE 3.1
The Beaufort Wind Scale

Beaufort Number	Name	Wind (knots)	Speed $(m\,s^{-1})$	State of the Sea Surface	Wave Height* (m)
0	Calm	<1	0–0.2	Sea like a mirror	0
1	Light airs	1–3	0.3–1.5	Ripples with the appearance of scales; no foam crests	0.1–0.2
2	Light breeze	4–6	1.6–3.3	Small wavelets; crests have glassy appearance but do not break	0.3–0.5
3	Gentle breeze	7–10	3.4–5.4	Large wavelets; crests begin to break; scattered white horses	0.6–1.0
4	Moderate breeze	11–16	5.5–7.9	Small waves, becoming longer; fairly frequent white horses	1.5
5	Fresh breeze	17–21	8.0–10.7	Moderate waves taking longer form; many white horses and chance of some spray	2.0
6	Strong breeze	22–27	10.8–13.8	Large waves forming; white foam crests extensive everywhere and spray probable	3.5
7	Moderate gale	28–33	13.9–17.1	Sea heaps up and white foam from breaking waves begins to be blown in streaks; spin-drift begins to be seen	5.0
8	Fresh gale	34–40	17.2–20.7	Moderately high waves of greater length; edges of crests break into spindrift; foam is blown in well-marked streaks	7.5
9	Strong gale	41–47	20.8–24.4	High waves; dense streaks of foam; sea begins to roll; spray may affect visibility	9.5
10	Whole gale	48–55	24.5–28.4	Very high waves with over-hanging crests; sea surface takes on white appearance as foam in great patches is blown in very dense streaks; rolling of sea is heavy and visibility reduced	12.0
11	Storm	56–64	28.5–32.7	Exceptionally high waves; sea covered with long patches of foam; small and medium sized ships might be lost from view behind waves for long times; visibility further reduced	15.0
12	Hurricane	>64	>32.7	Air filled with foam and spray; sea completely white with driving spray; visibility greatly reduced	>15

*Here, wave height is taken to mean the average of the highest one-third of the waves.

As wind speed varies with height above the sea surface, see Figure 3.5, the band of wind speeds relating to the Beaufort number are defined for a height of six metres above the sea.

Although regions of the ocean vary, the general probability of finding winds of any particular strength as a function of time is given in Figure 3.6. Light airs are not common, moderate breezes (about $6\,m\,s^{-1}$ or 14 knots) are the most common with stronger winds becoming progressively rarer with increasing speed.

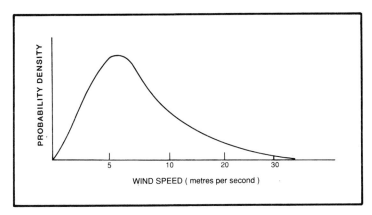

FIG. 3.6   General Probability of Encountering Winds of Specific
Speeds

The Effects of Wind on Equipment

The effect of the wind on the ship's equipment is usually indirect, either as a result of the waves which wind produces, or the icing which accompanies the wind and spray in polar latitudes. Strong winds may make station keeping difficult, and this may affect the performance of the ship as a weapon system. The direct effect of strong, steady winds or gusts on the antennae must be taken into account. However, the effects of blast are generally more severe; so that equipment designed to withstand, say, nuclear blast waves, will survive the worst wind conditions.

Deck operations can be extremely difficult and hazardous in strong winds, principally because they are associated with violent ship motion. Even if deck motion is not significant, winds of $10\,m\,s^{-1}$ (fresh breeze) can make operations difficult on a wet and slippery deck. Stronger winds associated with a violent storm ($30\,m\,s^{-1}$) can blow personnel overboard.

High winds may cause poor performance of such weapons as *chaff*, which may be dispersed too rapidly. Even if not limited by ship motion, helicopter and aircraft operations may be curtailed by strong winds.

Novel hull forms, such as the Small Water Plane Area Twin Hull (*SWATH*), to be described later, which are chosen because of their small motions, may be limited ultimately by their high windage, or the difficulties their complement will experience in operating the deck equipment in high winds.

Wave Theory

Although the main interest in this chapter is on the waves generated by winds, the sea can be disturbed by other periodic motions, forced by gravitational attraction of the Sun and Moon, or by the seismic events mentioned in Chapter 1, for instance. It is useful to put these wind-generated waves into the context of all the wave-like motions which can perturb the sea surface. Figure 3.7 should be referred to for the graphical description of terms used in the description of waves; these are defined in Table 3.2.

TABLE 3.2
Wave Parameters and Terms (see also Figure 3.7)

a	=	wave amplitude
H	=	wave height, equal to twice the amplitude
T	=	wave period; the time taken for a wave to pass a given point
f	=	wave frequency; $1/T$
L	=	wave length
η	=	elevation of water surface from rest position
c	=	wave speed, equal to $1.56T$ or $(gL/2\pi)^{\frac{1}{2}}$ in deep water or $(gd)^{\frac{1}{2}}$ in shallow water, where d = water depth and g = acceleration due to gravity $(9.8\,\mathrm{m\,s^{-2}})$
c_g	=	group speed, equal to $c/2$
H/L	=	wave steepness
E	=	total wave energy per unit area, given as $1/8\varrho g H^2$ where ϱ = water density

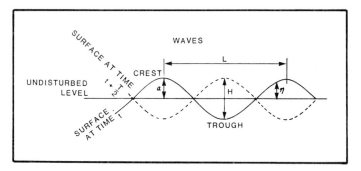

FIG. 3.7   Wave Motion and Terms

Figure 3.8 shows the total energy density of the surface in terms of the frequency or period of the wave motion; wind, atmospheric pressure systems, gravitational attraction and seismic events generate the waves. The forces controlling the waves once generated are gravity, surface tension and the Coriolis force. Surface tension is only important for the capillary waves or small ripples with wave lengths of less than 1.78 cm. For wind waves, only gravity has any effect on the wave profile; for the storm surges, tsunamis and tides, gravity and the Coriolis force control the wave

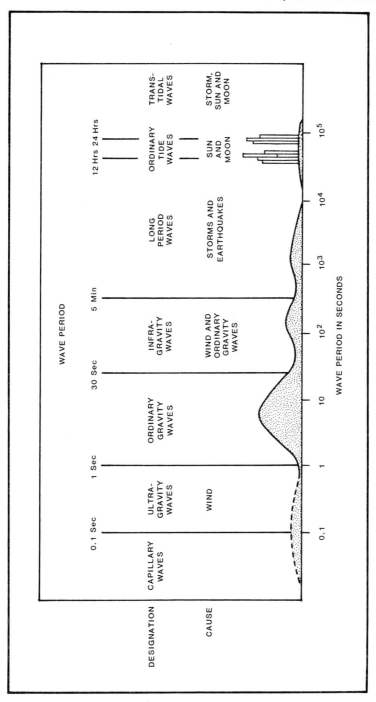

Fig. 3.8 Energy Density Spectrum of the Ocean Surface

characteristics. It can be seen from the diagram that the majority of the ocean's surface energy is in the wind waves, with periods between 1 to 30s.

It is the wind wave that the ship designer has to understand when building a vessel, and it is on these waves that the remainder of the chapter will concentrate.

In an area of wind, waves of a whole range of frequencies are generated, and propagate outwards. Waves of closely related frequencies interfere with each other and the net result is a wave *group* or packet of wave energy. These wave packets travel at one half the speed of the waves of the dominant frequency, which is known as the *group speed*, any individual wave passes through the group, only to disappear at the leading edge of the group. The effect of adding two waves of slightly differing frequencies is shown in Figure 3.9, showing the overall envelope which defines the wave group. It is this envelope which travels at half the wave speed, and propagates the wave energy across the sea surface.

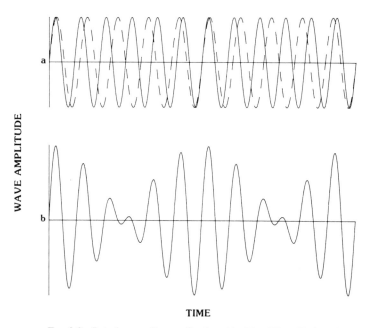

FIG. 3.9   Interference Pattern Produced by Two Wave Trains of
Very Similar Wave Lengths, Showing the Group Envelope

The speed of waves is given by the relationships in Table 3.2, for deep and shallow water. For deep water waves, it should be noted that waves with longer wave lengths (or greater periods) travel faster than shorter ones and if a group of waves are generated in a region, the longer wave lengths will move away from the region most quickly; this is known as *dispersion*.

A light breeze, blowing over the surface of the sea, produces disturbances which may barely be noticed. How these small ripples or capillary waves, sometimes called *cat's paws*, are formed is not fully understood, but the restoring force is surface tension. These ripples die out rapidly, tend to have rounded crests and have a wave velocity c greater than the group velocity c_g. (The formulae for wave and group speed given in Table 3.2 are only applicable to gravity waves.)

If the strength of the wind is such that these small disturbances exceed a certain size, for which the wave length, L, is 17 millimetres, then the dominant restoring force is that of gravity. As a consequence, above this wave length, the shape of the disturbances changes to that of a more crested wavelet and the group velocity exceeds the wave velocity by a factor of two. These larger wavelets are more durable than the ripples. Still stronger winds produce larger wavelets and waves. The formation of these waves is not a regular but a random process, and even small waves may have ripples superimposed upon them. The size of waves formed depends on the wind strength and for a given speed, a broad spectrum of wave lengths, wave heights and frequencies are produced.

Waves generated by local winds are termed a sea. They have sharp peaks and, typically, a crest to crest length of two to three times their wave length. As they move away from their area of generation, they change in nature, becoming more rounded and with a crest length typically six to seven times the wave length; these are the waves of a *swell*.

The distance over which the wind is able to blow is called the *fetch* and determines the amount of energy the atmosphere is able to impart to the sea surface. If the fetch is greater than about 500 kilometres, and the force of the wind is applied over a sufficiently long time, then the wave parameters reach maximum values and the sea is termed *fully-developed*. The figures for this fully-developed state are shown in Table 3.3 on page 65. The wave characteristics are also affected by nearby land, which imparts a vertical component to the wind, by the depth and the rate of change of the depth of water and the tidal conditions.

Although simple theories of wave motion allow waves to continue to increase indefinitely in height, with longer wave lengths and the same shape, in practice the wave length does not increase as rapidly and the seas become steeper and steeper. The mathematician Stokes showed that when the ratio of wave height to wave length exceeded 1:7, then the wave is no longer stable and breaks or spills over to form the well-known white caps. In the fully-developed sea state, the energy imparted by the wind to the sea surface is thus equal to the energy being dissipated by the waves through breaking. When tidal flow and wind direction are in opposition, rough seas are formed with an enhancement which is much greater than might be expected solely from the increase in apparent wind speed.

The speed of waves in shallow waters, where by 'shallow' we mean depths less than $L/20$ or two to 10 metres deep for typical wind waves, then the wave 'feels' the bottom. This is because wave motion on the surface results in a more or less circular motion of the individual water molecules. See Figure 3.10. (Note that for wave motion in any medium, the individual particles do not move forward, only the wave energy moves across the medium. This is not altogether true for water waves. In their case there is a slight net movement forward by water particles known as *Stokes' Drift*, but a cork floating on the water will only be seen to move up and down.)

Beneath the surface, these circular orbits become smaller and smaller. By a depth of $L/2$, the motion is negligible, hence the preference for submariners to travel below the sea surface whenever possible. In shallow water, these deep circular motions are

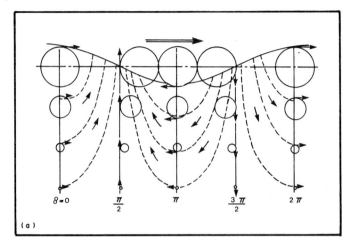

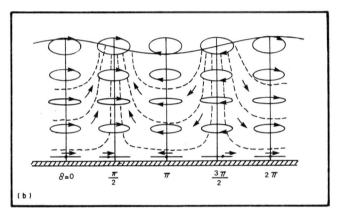

FIG. 3.10   Wave and Particle Motion in (a) Deep Water
and (b) Shallow Water

slowed by friction with the sea bed, the orbits become more elliptical. Wave speed
decreases, wave period remains the same, and by examining the relevant relationships, wave height must increase. Remembering that wave energy is proportional to
wave height *squared*, waves approaching a shoreline in storms have the potential to
do great damage; records note that on one occasion on the Scottish coast, 14 metre
high breakers moved seawall blocks of 2,600 tons.

Wave speed and group speed become the same in shallow water, the velocity is
given by a simple relationship dependent only on the water depth and the gravitation
constant:

$$c_g = c = (gd)^{\frac{1}{2}}$$

From this it may be seen that water waves slow up approaching the coastline. Their
direction of propagation can then be changed or *refracted* on entering shallow water

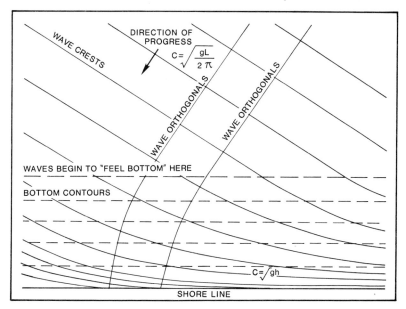

FIG. 3.11   Wave Refraction on Coastlines

at acute angles to the coast. This is the same behaviour as any wave motion on passing through a medium with one wave velocity into one of a different velocity; the apparent bending of a ruler immersed in a dish of water is a well-known example of refraction, using light waves. Figure 3.11 shows how the approaching wave train is refracted by the shallowing water; note how the wave crests, initially travelling at an angle to the coast, are 'steered' around so that they are finally parallel to the shoreline when they strike it.

Exactly the same effect can be seen if, instead of a headland, the wave train approaches a strong ocean current. Lateral shear in the current, as shown in Figure 3.12 can focus the energy of the wave train towards the centre of the current. This phenomenon is suspected to be working in the Agulhas Current, (Figure 4.6), along the coast of south-eastern Africa, where giant waves have been reported, not necessarily in storm conditions. These waves, typically 14 s period with wave lengths of 300 metres, heights of 20 metres, with their associated wave trough and steepened by refraction, are quite sufficient to sink large ships.

MATHEMATICS OF THE WIND WAVE

The naval architect has an interest in the range of waves possible, and the general sea states in which the vessel is to operate, but to understand the dynamics of the ship, a mathematical description of the water wave is needed.

Figure 3.13 shows an example of the highly irregular wave profile which is encountered in a wave generating region; when one observes the real sea surface, one might be able to distinguish some periodicity in the wave trains, but the general impression is of a complex and confused surface. This is extremely difficult both to describe and to model mathematically. The description requires the recently devel-

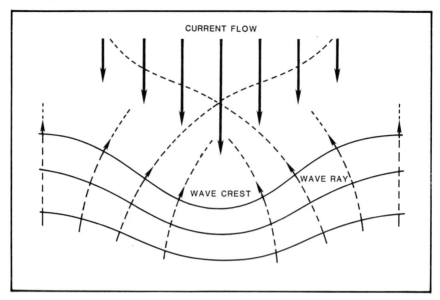

FIG. 3.12   Wave Refraction by Current Shear

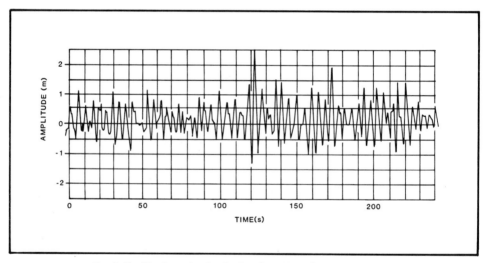

FIG. 3.13   The Irregular Sea Surface in a Wave Generating Region

oped branch of mathematics dealing with random variables. Some appreciation, however, of the general features can be obtained by considering a simple and readily described wave system. Mathematically, the simplest is a *sinusoidal wave* or *sine wave*, and a number of such waves, with varying parameters, can then be combined in an attempt to describe the real wave system. This is illustrated in Figure 3.14.

A particle exhibiting simple harmonic motion executes a sinusoidal motion which may be described by the equation:

$$x = a \sin(\omega t)$$

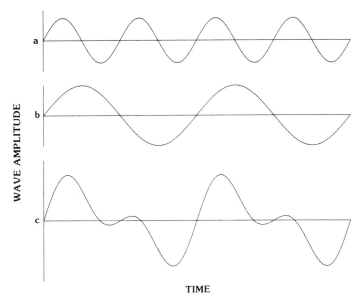

FIG. 3.14   The Addition of Sine Waves
Wave **a** and Wave **b** combine to form Wave **c**

where x is the distance from the mean position, a is the amplitude as before, ω the angular frequency and t the time.

This motion is only sinusoidal in time; the x projection of a particle rotating at a constant velocity in the XY plane is also described by this relationship. A sinusoidal wave can travel, in which case the shape of the wave is sinusoidal and moves in time. Figure 3.7 shows this wave. Individual particles on a string carrying such a wave are constrained in the x direction, each describes a simple harmonic type relation, but the wave disturbance travels in time because of the relative positions of the adjacent particles.

Sinusoidal waves in a fluid are slightly different from that on a string. There are no boundary conditions which confine the particles to the x direction. The solution for the motion is that of the *Laplace equation* for water of infinite depth. In this case the particles at the surface describe circles of radius $L/2$, and the equations of motion are known as the *Gerstner* or *Rankine wave*:

$$\eta_x = -ae^{kz} \sin(kx - \omega t)$$

η_x describes the motion of the water particles affected by the passage of the wave where the other symbols are z, the depth below the water's surface, ω the angular velocity of the wave and k the *wave number* defined as $2\pi/L$.

A term in surface tension could be included but such terms are negligible for significant sized waves. All particles of the fluid describe circles, with those at the surface having the largest radius. The radius decreases exponentially with depth, and at $z = L/2$, the motion is negligible. This was illustrated in Figure 3.10.

Trochoidal Wave Form

Although real seas can be described by a combination of sinusoidal wave forms, this is mathematically inconvenient. A single sinusoidal wave is too high for the wave length and a better, but more complex, approximation is a *trochoidal wave form*. This wave is the locus of a point fixed within a circle, as the circle is rolled along a straight line. The height of the wave is related to the distance of the fixed point from the centre of the circle, r, by the equation:

$$r = H/2$$

and the wave length by:

$$L = 2\pi R$$

where R is the radius of the circle. This is shown in Figure 3.15.

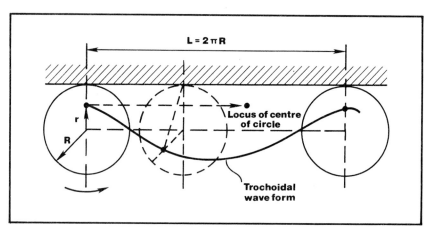

FIG. 3.15   Generation of a Trochoidal Wave Form

As in the case of the sinusoidal wave, particles on the surface describe a circular motion which decreases with depth exponentially. Because of the shape of the trochoidal wave, the locus of the centres of the circles generating the wave form (and hence the centre of rotation of the surface particles) does not coincide with the still water surface. It lies a distance $H^2/8R$ above it.

A standard trochoidal wave form is often adopted for checking the strength of a ship in a sea-way. The most usual choice is a wave with a wave length to height ratio of 20 (i.e. $r = L/40$) which approximately describes observed waves between 100 and 175 metres in length, but becomes progressively less realistic for longer waves as the height is exaggerated.

Open Ocean and Coastal Wave Spectra

The mathematical description of sinusoidal or trochoidal waves enables the principle of actual waves to be understood. For the purpose of predicting the motion of ships and the consequent performance degradation of equipment, it is necessary to use a statistical approach to combine numbers of sine waves if a realistic wave shape is to be generated. A real, complex sea may be considered as a superposition of a large number of sinusoidal waves of differing heights, frequencies and phases. The values chosen for these waves, and the weighting to be attached to them, must be related to empirical data. Comprehensive data giving a quantitative description of ocean waves is limited and the major source was a compilation of observations from merchant ships. This has been criticised as being unrepresentative—merchant ships, quite naturally, avoid storms! Recently, an environmental atlas* has been produced which should provide a sound basis for calculation throughout the NATO area of operations.

This atlas gives wave heights, frequencies and directions for many regions and correlates them with wind speed and direction. It has been found for each frequency band of waves, a number of possible amplitudes can occur, especially for coastal waves. However, mathematically this can be satisfactorily simplified to a *spectrum* which relates the mean amplitude (or alternatively, energy) of a wave to its frequency. The concept of a spectrum for a range of frequencies is illustrated in Figure 3.16.

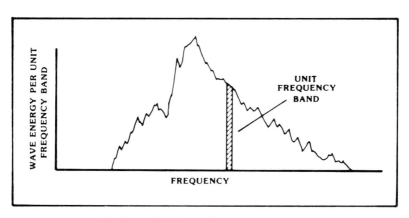

FIG. 3.16   The Energy/Frequency Spectrum

The form of the wave spectrum has been found to depend on how well the sea has developed. Newly generated wave systems have lower amplitude and higher mean frequency waves than a fully developed sea, which consists of larger, lower frequency waves, as illustrated in Figure 3.17.

If the wind dies down, the low frequency waves, with their higher velocity, move away from the area of generation, thereby contributing to swell in other parts of the ocean. This leaves the low amplitude, high frequency wave in the region of

*See Further Reading

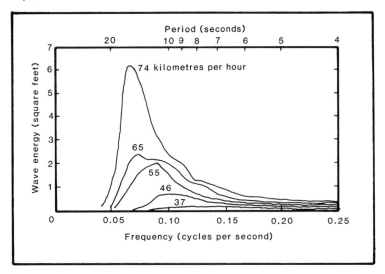

FIG. 3.17   The Spectrum of a Developed Sea

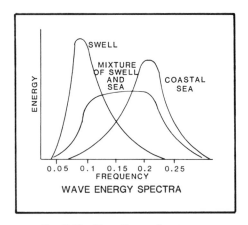

FIG. 3.18   Wave Energy Spectrum
for Coastal Seas

generation with a similar spectrum to that of a newly generated wave system. In coastal regions, such as the English Channel, a short fetch and variable winds give a coastal type spectrum of high frequency waves. To this must be added the Atlantic swell of low frequency waves; such a combination can lead to a spectrum of almost constant amplitude over a typical range of frequencies, see Figure 3.18.

The importance of the wind as a motivating force in wave generation has led to several attempts to relate wind speed and wave amplitude, especially for fully-developed seas where correlation may be expected to be more probable. Such work leads to the *Sea State Code* similar to the Beaufort Scale for the wind force. The Sea State Code adopted by the World Meteorological Organisation as an international standard is shown in Table 3.3. Code 0 applies to calm water, while code 9 is for phenomenal seas. Each code represents a band of *significant wave heights* where this term indicates the mean height of the highest one-third of all the waves. The height of

TABLE 3.3
Sea State Codes

Sea State Number	Significant Wave Height (m)		Sustained Wind Speed (knots)*	
	Range	Mean	Range	Mean
0 – 1	0 – 0.1	0.05	0 – 6	3
2	0.1 – 0.5	0.3	7 – 10	8.5
3	0.5 – 1.25	0.88	11 – 16	13.5
4	1.25 – 2.5	1.88	17 – 21	19
5	2.5 – 4	3.25	22 – 27	24.5
6	4 – 6	5	28 – 47	37.5
7	6 – 9	7.5	48 – 55	51.5
8	9 – 14	11.5	56 – 63	59.5
>8	>14	>14	>63	>63

*Sustained wind is that wind, which, if it is maintained for a long period over a sufficient fetch, will result in a fully developed sea with the significant wave heights shown.

the significant wave is not only of use in the standard spectra, but relates closely to the estimation of wave heights of a confused sea made by eye. The table also shows the approximate sustained wind speed, which, provided it blows for the correct duration and fetch to produce a fully developed sea, will result in waves of the significant wave height range equivalent to the sea state number.

THE EFFECT OF WAVES ON SHIP STRUCTURE

The considerable resources involved in the prediction and description of wave motion are of practical interest only in the way in which they can be used to predict the effect on the ship's structure or ship motion. Earlier, in Chapter 2, the concept of the centre of gravity (G) and the centre of buoyancy (B) of a ship in a calm sea was discussed. B is a representation of the integral buoyant effect of the whole immersed body and G is a representation of all the ship's weights and loads. In fact, the effect of buoyancy and the weight may not cancel each other out locally, only overall. Any local disparities may result in portions of the ship where there are net forces due to buoyancy or gravity. These net forces act to distort the structure.

A typical example is given in Figure 3.19 where the buoyancy dominates the central section of the ship with its large immersed volume. Towards the bow and stern, although the weight is less, the buoyancy is much reduced because of the finer *form* and the weight dominates. The resultant forces tend to make the vessel *hog*. In a sea-way, where the sea's surface is no longer flat, induced changes in the buoyancy also affect the ship's structure; a wave crest coinciding with the centre of the ship will also tend to cause hogging. Alternatively, if the wave crests occur towards the bow and stern, with a trough at the centre, then sagging will occur. Ships which are steaming at an angle to the predominant wave direction will also experience torsional distortion in the form suggested in Figure 3.20.

The movement of the ship's structure in a sea affects the alignment of weapons systems. The flexure of a ship can alter the sight angle of different elements of a weapon system, especially if they are far apart. Weapons are aligned in harbour or

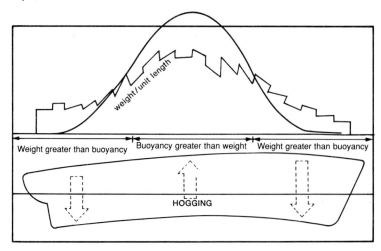

Fig. 3.19   Still Water Hogging

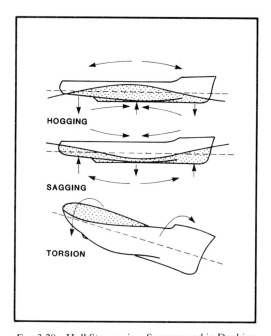

Fig. 3.20   Hull Stresses in a Sea-way and in Docking

calm water and the design of the systems must take into account ship flexure in the error budgets of information passed from, say, surveillance to tracking radars. Reduction of ship flexure by the provision of additional structure may not be possible, or even desirable.

The problem of alignment is exacerbated by extreme ship motion in rough seas, which, by itself, may result in a weapon operating close to its limits of error budget. Although it may be possible to compensate to some extent for ship motion, compensation for flexure is extremely difficult.

Apart from the short-term alignment problems arising from flexure, long-term misalignment may result from the working of a ship in a sea-way. A new ship embodies many stresses incorporated during building. During the launch, the structure experiences extreme stress, stresses which in some instances may be greater than any other which it may experience during its life. To these are added additional stresses resulting from the weights taken on board during the fitting out. Weapons aligned following build may therefore be found to be misaligned after the first major sea passage because, in the flexure and torsion of the vessel in heavy seas, the structure has been displaced slightly in the reduction of the inherent build stresses. Alignment checks of secondary datum points, bench marks and weapon systems must be undertaken several times early in a ship's life to ensure accurate operation. Similar stresses, although not of the same magnitude, may be imposed by dry docking.

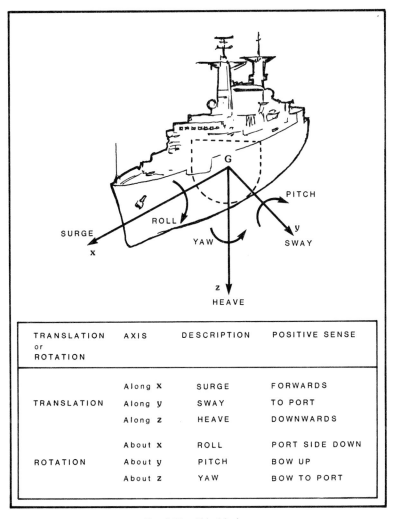

TRANSLATION or ROTATION	AXIS	DESCRIPTION	POSITIVE SENSE
	Along x	SURGE	FORWARDS
TRANSLATION	Along y	SWAY	TO PORT
	Along z	HEAVE	DOWNWARDS
	About x	ROLL	PORT SIDE DOWN
ROTATION	About y	PITCH	BOW UP
	About z	YAW	BOW TO PORT

Fig. 3.21   Ship Motions

Seakeeping

A ship has six degrees of freedom in its motion, and waves acting on the vessel can induce motion in all six. These are shown in Figure 3.21. Because of the nature of forces produced by waves, the major motions are the rotational ones; these are rotation in the transverse vertical plane (rolling) and the fore and aft vertical (or longitudinal) plane (pitching). Less important is rotation in the horizontal plane (yawing). Waves can also displace the ship linearly in motions which may be vertical (heaving), fore and aft (surging) and athwartships (swaying), although heaving is the most significant.

Waves of different frequency will affect the ship in different ways. For instance, waves whose wave length are much smaller than the ship will have little effect, whereas waves with wave length comparable to the length of the ship will cause pitching, see Figure 3.22. (Such waves will also produce the greatest hogging and sagging.) Waves much larger than the ship's length will cause extreme pitching as the vessel follows the wave passing beneath it. The motion resulting from waves of a given frequency are described by the *Response Amplitude Operator*; Figure 3.23 shows the Operators for the principal motions. It will be noted that the Operator for rolling is particularly sharp with the peaks at the natural frequency of oscillation of the ship. This indicates that the effect of waves at about this frequency is amplified because it stimulates a resonant response.

FIG. 3.22   Pitching in a Small Warship (*Crown Copyright/RN Photo*)

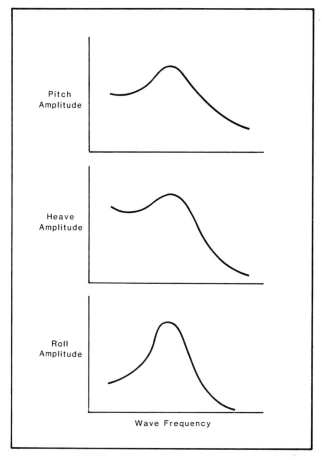

Pitch
Amplitude

Heave
Amplitude

Roll
Amplitude

Wave Frequency

FIG. 3.23   Typical Response Amplitude Operator
Curves

The sea spectrum gives the significance of a given frequency in forcing the motions of a ship. In combination with the Response Amplitude Operator, it gives the response of the vessel to that frequency and the expected motion in the sea-way described by the spectrum. Figure 3.24 shows how the Operator and the sea wave spectrum are combined to form the predicted ship motion. In predicting the motion, it is also important to consider the direction of the waves.

Speed

The speed of a vessel has a significant effect on motion, especially pitching. (Mathematically, this is treated by modifying the effective wave spectrum to that of the *encounter spectrum*.) In heavy seas the resistance to motion increases and therefore greater power is required in rough, as opposed to calm, waters for the same speed. In Sea State 5 or above, it is necessary, however, to reduce the speed of the ship below that which it could theoretically achieve with the power available. The principal reason for this speed reduction is to reduce the extreme pitching (or, with a

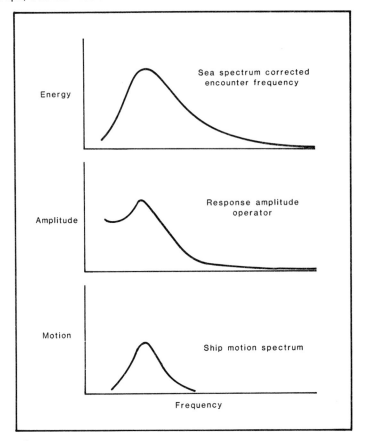

Energy

Sea spectrum corrected
encounter frequency

Amplitude

Response amplitude
operator

Motion

Ship motion spectrum

Frequency

FIG. 3.24   Wave Energy Spectrum and Response of a Ship in
an Irregular Sea (Illustrated for Heave)

quartering sea, the extreme pitching and rolling). This pitching is not only unpleasant for the ship's complement, but can lead to the emergence of the bow sonars or the propellers, which can damage the former and further reduce speed with the latter. Although bow sonars have hydrodynamic advantages over others in calm seas, at moderate operating speeds this is partially offset by the problem of pitching in long waves.

A further limitation on the ship's speed is the onset of *slamming*. This irregular motion is difficult to predict but it occurs when large areas of almost flat plating on the forward end of the vessel meet a wave at an acute angle. The ship's motion is suddenly halted and the ship shudders. The energy dissipated in checking the motion results in a large bang and flexural vibrations. Slamming not only produces a motion which is unpleasant but can provide severe structural damage if it is allowed to continue for long periods. Slamming affects weapons systems because it introduces vibration in forward areas (where vibration is rarely experienced and consequently not considered as important for equipment mounted there). Weapons systems which require motion prediction to achieve their performance can be severely affected by the irregular motion of slamming.

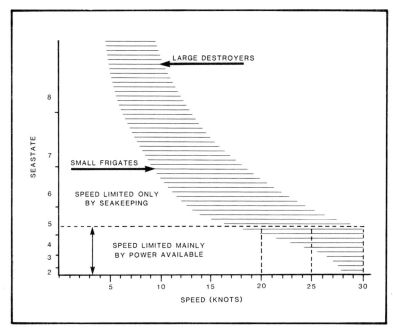

Fig. 3.25   Ship Speed Versus Sea State for Frigates and Destroyers

In general, the longer the vessel, the less are the effects of pitching and slamming, and consequently the higher the speed it can maintain in a given sea state. This is illustrated in Figure 3.25 for frigates and destroyers, showing the typical range of speeds limited by engine power and by sea state.

Another effect related to high sea states is that of *deck wetness*. In severe weather, bow immersion results in the shipping of water over the *forecastle*. See Figure 3.26. Although, on occasions, such shipping of *green seas* (solid masses of water rather than spray), may obscure vision from the bridge windows, there is evidence that such deck wetness does not in itself result in reduction of the ship's speed, even for frigates. However, the stresses set up as a result of shipping green seas can damage the deck mounted equipment. Guns and launchers mounted at the fore ends require protection of V-shaped breakwaters, and where these fail to provide protection, there is danger of damage or equipment being carried away.

Data provided by the United States Navy for the North Atlantic indicate that there are limits to the speed of operation by severe weather for a considerable proportion of the time. A 120 metre frigate would only be capable of operating in the Greenland–Iceland–United Kingdom gap, (60–65°N), at full power during about 60 per cent of the summer and less than 30 per cent of the winter. This is shown in Figure 3.27. Anti-Submarine Warfare (ASW) vessels fitted with bow sonar domes are particularly sensitive to slamming as noted previously and, consequently, experience speed reduction more often. They are able to operate effectively at lower speeds unless the weather is very bad, as shown in Figure 3.27. ASW craft must have a speed advantage over ships in company if they are to conduct their operations effectively. Speed limitations imposed by sea state upon ASW escorts may therefore limit the speed of advance of convoys or task forces.

FIG. 3.26   Deck Wetness (*Crown Copyright/RN Photo*)

Design Techniques for Reduction of Motion

Vessels which have small resultant motions are said to have *good seakeeping*. More specifically, ships which have motions which are small and confined primarily to those which affect the crew least, are termed *sea kindly*. A reduction in the motions can be achieved by making the vessel larger; increasing the length of the ship, for instance, reduces pitching and allows more severe seas to be experienced before it is necessary to reduce speed. Increasing length on the other hand can increase the effects of hogging and sagging unless it is accompanied by increased structural strength. Pitching can also be reduced by prudent choice of hull form, especially in the shape of the bow; a long pointed V-shaped bow enables the ship to cut through the water easily and flare reduces the pitching movement. A typical shape for the forward end of a warship is shown in Figure 3.28.

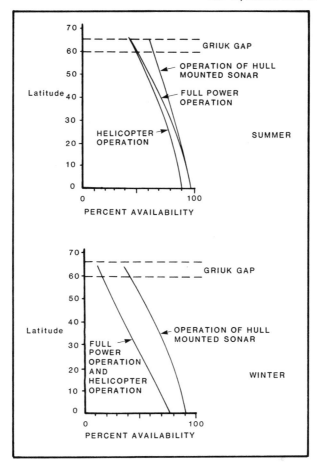

Fig. 3.27   Typical Availability of Hull Mounted
Sonar Operations in the North Atlantic

Roll is generally less easy to reduce by the choice of hull form, although hulls with flare roll less than the slab-sided ones. The *GZ* curve for a ship with flare is steeper for small angles of heel as the immersed volume increases more quickly. The resulting roll may, however, be at a less favourable frequency. A number of systems are used to reduce roll and produce a more suitable weapons platform. The term *stable platform* is used for a vessel with low motions, especially low roll amplitudes. This term refers to the Response Amplitude Operator and the *induced motions*, and should not be confused with the ability of the ship to return to the vertical when it has experienced a heeling moment. In the first case, the problem is one of dynamic motion, whereas in the second, the considerations are of the quasi-static situation described in Chapter 2. The effects are related in a complex fashion as the natural frequency of the roll depends on the static stability of the ship.

The natural period of roll depends, to a first approximation, on the rate of change of *GZ* as the ship heels. In general, ships with a low static stability margin will have a long roll period and, because their roll is forced by the rarer low frequency waves,

Fig. 3.28   Long Narrow Bows for Pitch Reduction (*Crown Copyright/RN Photo*)

will experience lower amplitude roll motions. Ships with the lower static stability margin make the most effective weapons platforms. This results in a dichotomy for the designer. If a large stability margin which will allow additional weapons and equipment to be fitted during the life of a warship is provided, then for the first years of its operation, excessive roll may be experienced, and the performance of the complement, weapons, and aircraft will be severely degraded.

Equipment for Reducing Roll Motions

The reduction of roll motions is so important that several systems have been developed which aim to reduce roll amplitudes. Most major warships (and most passenger vessels) are fitted with fin stabilisers (again the term *stabilisation* may cause some confusion—it refers to the stabilisation, or damping, of the motion, and not to the stability of the ship). The fins, see Figure 3.29, are a pair of short stubby wing-like appendages fitted to either side of the vessel which can be tilted to counteract the roll forces. One fin (on the side to which the ship is rolling) will be tilted up to provide lift, and the other fin will be tilted down; as the ship's motion continues and the roll reverses, then the fin angles are reversed. To provide lift, there must be, as with the wings of an aircraft, flow over the fin stabilisers, which are consequently not effective at slower speeds. A motion sensing and fin control and activation systems are required for operation.

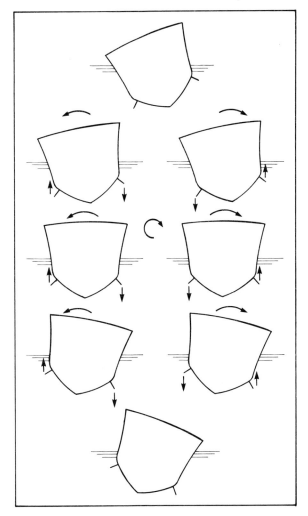

FIG. 3.29   Active Fin Stabilisation System Fitted
to Larger Vessels

Roll reduction in ships which operate at low speeds is achieved by horizontal movement of G to counter the roll motion. Such systems may be *active* and vary G by physically moving weights or fluids using a sensor and control system. See Figure 3.30. In the latter case, the volume of fluid (usually water) which must be moved is large, and can be achieved by large pumps, pressurised air systems or by moving swash plates. The *Tripartite Minehunter*, which is small and must travel at low speeds during mine hunting operations, uses such a fluid system.

Alternatively, a *passive* roll reduction system can be used; these could be bilge keels, fixed fins or a passive tank system. Bilge keels are keels fitted to either side of the ship's bottom, along one-half to two-thirds of the vessel's length. They have a small resistance to forward motion in calm water and a higher resistance to roll, reducing the roll amplitude by typically 35 per cent. Unfortunately, the resistance to

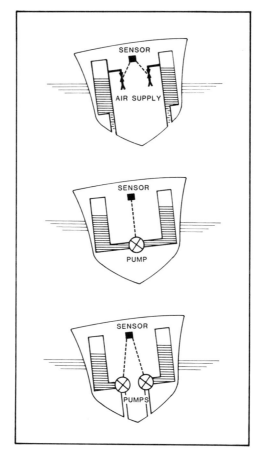

FIG. 3.30   Active Tank System for Roll
Reduction

forward motion increases when the ship is rolling and this considerably increases the power requirement in a sea-way. Fixed fins are similar to bilge keels, but do not extend so far along the ship's length and protrude further from the ship's side (thereby making them more liable to damage and cause difficulty in docking). It is claimed that because of the shape, they cause less drag at high speeds than bilge keels, but they are less effective at low speeds.

The passive tank system allows liquid (again, usually water) to flow between tanks through connecting tubes of high impedance or resistance to flow, see Figure 3.31. By adjusting this impedance, it is possible to arrange for the effect of the water's motion to be out of phase with, and lag behind, the ship's motion. At one particular frequency, the motion will be damped. At other frequencies, the roll amplitude may be increased because of the free surface effect of the water in the tanks. Provided the impedance is chosen carefully, this system will damp the high amplitude of the natural roll frequency and the enhancement of the small roll amplitudes experienced at other frequencies will be acceptable. Passive weight systems have been proposed, but are heavier than passive tank systems of the same effectiveness.

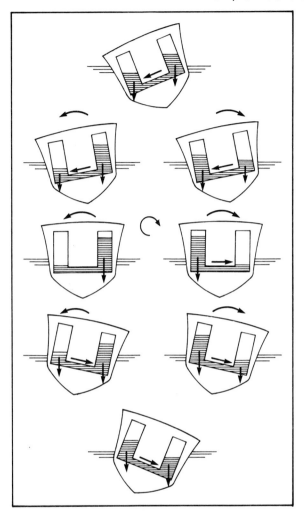

Fig. 3.31   Passive Tank System for Roll Reduction

A comparison of the effectiveness of all the roll stabilisation systems is given in Table 3.4.

TABLE 3.4
Comparison of Stabilising Systems

Type	Active Fin	Passive Tank	Active Tank	Bilge Keel
EFFECTIVENESS	90%	60–70%	unknown	35%
LOW SPEED OPERATION	poor	good	good	poor
POWER REQUIREMENTS	small	none	large	none
COST	high	moderate	high	low
MAINTENANCE	moderate	low	moderate	moderate

Motion Effects on Ship's Complement

In addition to affecting the ship, the performance of the ship's company in heavy weather will be degraded. The ability to move quickly will be impaired by the rolling and pitching of the ship with the necessity to hold on to retain balance. This will limit tasks such as re-arming helicopters, reloading missile tubes and carrying out repairs to equipment. Work on upper decks may be constrained, with some areas out of bounds, because of the dangers of being swept overboard. Tasks involving the movement of heavy equipment also become highly dangerous in a violently moving ship.

Of great significance, of course, is the detrimental effect of sea sickness on performance. Tasks requiring concentration, precision or manual dexterity become difficult when ill with motion sickness. Modern warships depend increasingly on the performance of such skills, a problem which is exacerbated by trends to smaller hull forms. The effects of sea sickness are, unfortunately, well known to most people who have been to sea in heavy weather: feelings of nausea, listlessness and vomiting. These symptoms are a result of disturbances to the vestibula and the labyrinthine system of the inner ear which sense and control balance. Many factors influence sea sickness: tiredness, hunger, cold, low morale and fear can all increase the propensity as can witnessing others being sick, or certain odours such as fuel oil or diesel exhaust. As might be expected, there is some correlation between sea sickness and certain motions—principally the linear acceleration caused by pitch and heave and the angular acceleration caused by roll. The frequency of motion is a vital factor; Figure 3.32 shows that roll periods greater than two seconds, which occur in ships with high GM, result in high incidences of sea sickness. The frequency and amplitude of the motion can be combined to give a subjective motion level which can be used to predict the incidence of sea sickness amongst the ship's complement. The propensity to motion sickness is also a personal characteristic, as is the ability to become acclimatised. Studies have indicated that half the crew might be expected to be sea sick on the first day at sea, 15 per cent on the second and 10 per cent of the crew for a week.

The effects of sea motion can be reduced by drugs, but some of these, while suppressing nausea, can cause drowsiness. This will not improve the performance of tasks requiring mental alertness such as confirmation of the warfare picture or assessment of threat in the Operations Room. The motions causing sickness are lowest close to the centre of the ship and the designer can ensure that difficult tasks are performed with the greatest effectiveness by ensuring that the Ops room, control room and offices are sited in that part of the ship. This area is also of value for accommodation; moving crew quarters to a more lively part of the ship may increase tiredness and loss of performance.

The techniques described earlier, active or passive roll stabilisation, can be used to reduce the angular acceleration contribution to roll. It is difficult to achieve the correct balance between cost and complexity and the reduction in roll, because of the problems of quantitatively assessing the incidence and effects of sea sickness. Justification for these techniques is generally made on the grounds of increased equipment performance supported by the increased ability of the crew to carry out their tasks.

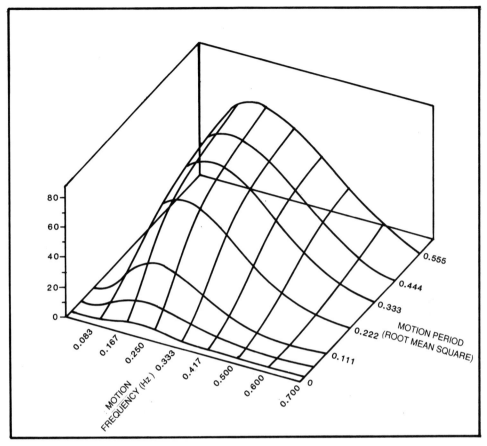

FɪɢG. 3.32   Motion Sickness Incidence

Effect of Motion on Equipment

The performance of equipment is affected by heavy seas in a number of ways. A ship which is moving violently may move into the path of a missile or shell fired close to its limit of clear arc. As a consequence, clear arcs must be reduced to account for heavy weather. It has already been noted that ship's flexure caused by high seas can affect weapon alignment. We have also seen that pitching can result in emergence of bow sonars, with degradation of performance and possible damage; even air entrained during vigorous motion can affect sonar sensitivity. To allow for the possible damage caused by deck wetness and green seas, equipment for the forecastle must be extremely sturdy.

Table 3.5 shows the typical motions for a roll-stabilised ship of 5,000 tonnes. Equipment such as radars and launchers are stabilised in order to compensate for the moderate motions of a roll-stabilised vessel. A radar may be stabilised to say, seven degrees of roll; extreme motions exceeding this angle will cause the radar to meet the end stops and the performance will suffer. In considering whether stabilisation at greater angles is cost effective, it must be remembered that increasing angles of roll

TABLE 3.5
Motions for a Ship of about 5,000 tonnes

Condition	Motion	Amplitude	Period (s)
Extreme motions	Roll	±25°	9–10
	Pitch	±7°	6
	Heave	±3 m	6
Moderate motions	Roll (stabilised)	±6°	9–10
	Pitch	±5°	6
	Heave	±1.5 m	6

become progressively less likely. In addition, increasing the angular range over which the equipment is stabilised becomes progressively more expensive, involving heavier and more powerful stabilising motors to accommodate the more rapid rates of change of motion (which from a designer's point of view may be as important as the maximum angle). It is also essential that all the elements are matched; there is little point in increasing the performance of, say, a tracking radar, if the launcher limits the performance of the overall system. It may therefore be more cost effective to decrease the roll of the ship rather than increasing the cost of individual items of equipment, as all the weapons systems (and the crew) gain from improvements to the ship's seakeeping.

One factor which is paramount in considering the effect of ship motion is the area of operation. In the higher latitudes, the weather is generally worse than in lower latitudes, especially in winter, and the ability to operate in high sea states is more valuable in these regions. For instance, the loss of performance of equipment in Sea State 5 is unimportant close to the equator, as such conditions are rarely encountered there. However, in the northern North Atlantic, at about 50°N, the difference between being able to operate at Sea State 4 and low Sea State 5 would reduce the time available from 70 per cent to 50 per cent. In this case, the gains from using more costly equipment or bigger ships (or both) are thus considerable in terms of availability.

The performance of equipment in heavy weather may be reduced by factors other than merely ship motion. The performance of radar may be degraded in high sea states, especially for low angles of depression because of high 'sea clutter'. This is the scattering of the radar signal by the wave tops, producing spurious echoes on the radar screen. Radars are also affected by precipitation, both rain and snow, which often accompanies the high winds. These factors exacerbate the problems of tracking a target from a rapidly moving platform. The streaming and recovery of *towed array sonars* are difficult above low Sea State 5, but operations may continue into slightly higher sea states once the equipment is deployed.

Helicopters and aircraft operations are severely limited by ship motions and high winds, but vessels which are fitted with devices which catch and hold a landing helicopter such as RAST or BEARTRAP allow them to be recovered and landed in higher sea states than normally possible. Traditionally, helicopter and aircraft operations have required vessels to change direction to minimise the effects of motion and wind. If the ship is operating an ASW towed array, this may not always be possible and this further limits the availability of such vessels in bad weather.

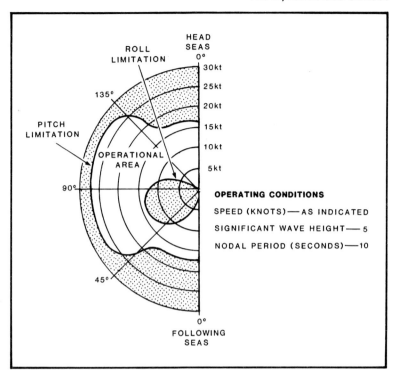

FIG. 3.33   Typical Limit of Operation Diagram for Helicopter Operations
from a Warship in a Sea-way

Some evolutions such as *Replenishment at Sea* (RAS) are also severely limited by high sea states. Although such tasks are essential to support naval operations, there is a greater flexibility in their timing and there must be a distinction between operations which are essential at all times, and those which may be deferred, albeit with some penalty. There are indications that during the winter in the northern North Atlantic, ships of frigate size (120 metres) may only be able to undertake RAS on about half of the possible occasions.

To summarise the equipment weather restrictions for frigates; the limitations of operations of a hull mounted sonar are Sea State 4–5 and, for helicopter operations, Sea State 4. By increasing the length of the vessel to about 150 metres, these limits would increase to low Sea State 5. The indications are, however, that effective ASW operations, requiring both bow sonar and helicopter, may be possible from a frigate in the northern North Atlantic during the winter for only 15 per cent of the time. In order to maximise the effectiveness of a warship, the Royal Navy uses diagrams like Figure 3.33. This shows the speeds and directions in which a vessel may operate whilst carrying out particular evolutions.

Icing

Icing of upper deck equipment is produced by the combination of breaking waves and high winds in freezing weather. The ice formed, see Figure 3.34, can severely

FIG. 3.34   Icing on the Upper Decks (*Author's Photo*)

increase the weight of unprotected trackers and launchers and prevent their operation, as well as straining communications antennae. Icing on equipment can be prevented by means of de-icing heaters or flexible rubber covers which can be pressurised with air at regular intervals to break the covering of ice.

Ice on the upper deck can severely reduce the stability of the ship because of the additional top weight. Several Arctic trawlers are thought to have foundered due to the build-up of ice. It may be necessary in such conditions to de-ice the mast and upper deck with steam hoses.

Future Hull Forms

A dramatic reduction in ship motion can be obtained for a given length of vessel by building a small water plain area twin hull (SWATH), see Figure 3.35. The configuration of such vessels is usually two submerged cylindrical floats, connected by means of struts to a platform which carries the superstructure and upper deck equipment. Experimental versions of such vessels are currently in operation with the United States Coast Guard. Currently there are no plans to build a large warship in this configuration. The high cost of embarking on risky new technology of this kind acts as a strong disincentive.

For small vessels operating in the lower sea states, a hydrofoil offers operations advantages in both speed and reduction of ship motions. They are, however, costly and have low endurance when compared with displacement vessels. Several navies have evaluated such craft but as yet they have not come into widespread use. For

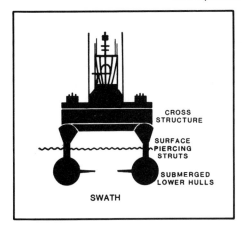

FIG. 3.35   SWATH Hull

FIG. 3.36   Typical Naval Hydrofoil: the Italian *NIBBIO* (*Crown Copyright/Navy International*)

FIG. 3.37   Military Hovercraft: the BH-7 (*Crown Copyright/RN Photo*)

similar reasons, hovercraft have similar operational advantages and disadvantages and find more use in troop and landing evolutions.

CONCLUSIONS

In all but extreme sea conditions, operation of a warship is possible, given good initial design and suitable equipment. This presupposes that the vessel is being used in the region for which she has been designed; for working outside this environment, considerable expenditure on equipment modification or limitations of vessel availability must be accepted.

4

The Deep Ocean and the Coastal Seas

It was shown earlier that the heat of the Sun drove the atmospheric circulation and that the atmosphere and oceans together provided the mechanism for transporting heat from the equator to the poles. The surface waves generated by the winds were shown to influence ship design. The intention of this chapter is to illustrate the other aspect of the transport process, and to describe the motion of the deep ocean and the processes working in the coastal seas which link with the deep ocean systems.

The wind itself drives some of this circulation, direct solar heating and tidal currents are responsible for the rest of the transport. These forces generate water masses with differing salt and heat content, and thus different densities; gravity and the horizontal wind stress move the ocean waters, driving the deep and the surface currents, distributing the heat and the dissolved salts around the globe, in the deep ocean and along the coastlines of the coastal seas.

Submarines use these differing characteristics of temperature and salinity of sea water to hide in the ocean, and anti-submarine forces need to measure these parameters to find their targets. More and more, the oceans are seen to be part of a coherent whole; pollution intentionally or accidentally discharged in one ocean, can arrive on some other countries' beaches. Wastes deposited in the deep ocean, on the abyssal plains for instance, must be proved to be in a safe repository. Sewage or chemical effluents discharged into rivers end up in the coastal seas which may border several countries. A basic understanding of the coherent motion of the world ocean water mass, the circulation of the oceans, and the behaviour of the coastal seas is needed to help formulate the requirements for a maritime commitment.

THE SUBDIVISIONS OF THE OCEANS

Examining the temperature,* salinity and density of the water column in a typical ocean at three locations, polar, temperate and tropical, as shown in Figure 4.1, from the surface to the bottom, the profiles show three distinct zones. In the surface, down

---

*This discussion relates to the *in situ* temperature or the actual observed temperature. If water is brought to the surface without exchanging heat with the surrounding water (known as adiabatic movement) the decrease in pressure would allow the water to expand and its temperature would decrease. The temperature that this water parcel would have at atmospheric pressure is known as the *potential temperature*. As this temperature is independent of pressure, and hence of depth, it is often used when comparing characteristics of deep waters. The potential temperature can be calculated knowing the depth, salinity and *in situ* temperature of the original observation.

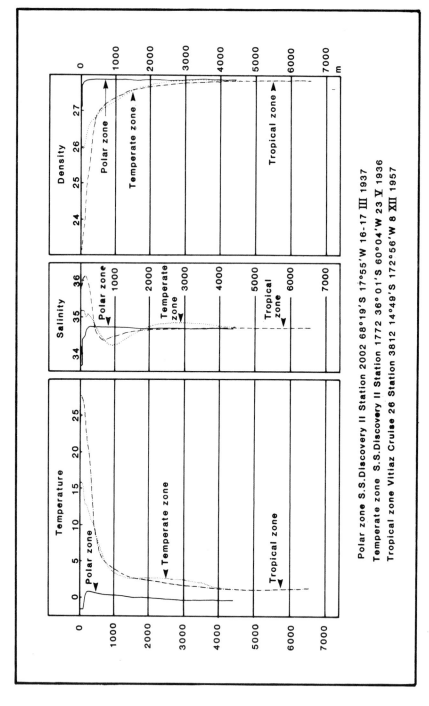

Polar zone S.S.Discovery II Station 2002 68°19'S 17°55'W 16-17 III 1937
Temperate zone S.S.Discovery II Station 1772 36°01'S 60°04'W 23 V 1936
Tropical zone Vitiaz Cruise 26 Station 3812 14°49'S 172°56'W 8 XII 1957

Fig. 4.1   Temperature, Salinity and Density Profiles with Depth at Three Oceanic Locations, Polar, Temperate and Tropical

to about 100 metres depth, the temperatures are high in the warmer climates, between 15 and 20 degrees C with values of salinity in excess of 35.

The corresponding surface densities are low, $1,023 \, \text{kg m}^{-3}$. The high temperatures are the result of solar heating, the high salinities from the excess of evaporation over precipitation, which leaves the salt behind in the surface waters. It is interesting to note that although this excess salt increases the density of the surface sea water, the increase in temperature more than compensates to lower the density values. The surface waters are consequently much lighter than the waters beneath.

Values for temperature and salinity are fairly constant in these surface waters down to depths around 100 metres. This zone is known as the *surface mixed-layer* as the water is kept well-mixed by the stirring induced by wind-waves (see Figure 3.10) and surface currents. In the coastal seas, where depths are of the same order as the deep ocean mixed-layer, the same turbulent processes, with the addition of tidal currents, keep the water well-stirred from the surface to the bottom. However, the semi-enclosed nature of some of these coastal waters allow much higher temperatures to develop, values up to 40 degrees C can be found in the northern seas and gulfs of the Indian Ocean.

Below these surface waters, temperature falls off very rapidly, salinity decreases and density increases. The depth range, where values change rapidly is known as the *permanent thermocline*, denoting the rapid decrease in temperature from the surface values to those at 1,000 metres. By analogy, the same zone is also called the *pycnocline* denoting the rapid increase in density. Superimposed on the permanent thermocline, there can be a seasonal, or even daily thermoclines, see Figure 4.2. Between 1,000 and 2,000 metres deep, there is some variation in temperature and a greater variation in salinity. Below 2,000 metres, these three parameters have stabilised and, although they continue in the same decreasing trend, the values change little all the way to the ocean floor. Bottom temperatures are of the order of two degrees C, salinities around 34.7 and densities, $1,028 \, \text{kg m}^{-3}$. This lower section

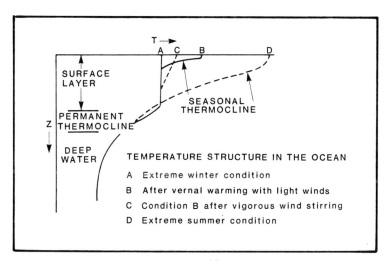

FIG. 4.2   The Seasonal and Daily Thermoclines Superimposed on the Permanent Thermocline in Ocean Surface Waters

of the water column represents the bulk of the ocean water mass; the mean temperature of the world ocean is only 3.5 degrees C and salinity 34.7.

Examining the polar curves, low, even sub-zero temperature water is found at the surface, with low salinities, both parameters rise slightly beneath the surface layer and remain almost constant all the way to the sea bed. Bottom temperatures are lower than minus one degree C, the salt content of the sea water has lowered the freezing point to values near minus two degrees C. Note there is no obvious thermocline or pycnocline in these polar waters.

By combining similar observations of temperature and salinity for a complete ocean, north to south, a general picture of the vertical subdivisions of the ocean can be constructed. Figure 4.3 shows the temperature and Figure 4.4 the salinity of the Atlantic Ocean, from the Antarctic continent to the Arctic Ocean.

From these two diagrams, one can draw a schematic picture of this ocean, showing

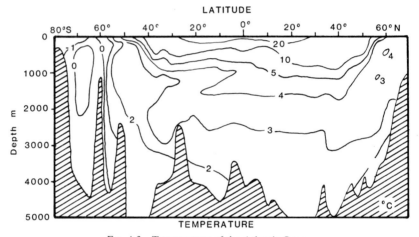

FIG. 4.3   Temperature of the Atlantic Ocean

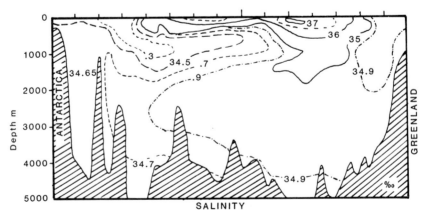

FIG. 4.4   Salinity of the Atlantic Ocean

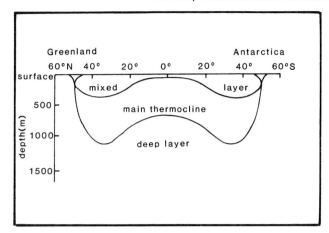

FIG. 4.5   The Vertical Subdivisions of the Ocean Water
Mass

the three major subdivisions of the water mass, the surface waters, the thermocline (or pycnocline) zone, and the deep water, as shown in Figure 4.5. The surface layer, approximately two per cent of the total water mass of the oceans is confined between 50°N or 50°S, and is warm and more saline; its depth is largely controlled by the extent that surface winds can mix the warmer water downwards. A situation where one light water mass sits on top of another more dense water body has less potential energy than a single, mixed water mass of the two combined; energy has to be supplied to mix the surface with the deep water. This mixing is ultimately inhibited by the thermocline layer where, as explained previously, the rapid fall-off in temperature effectively creates a stability barrier to further downward mixing of the surface layer. Conversely, the thermocline acts as a 'lid' for the deep water below, inhibiting upward transfer of water. It should be noted that the deep waters come up to the surface at both poles.

Values of temperature and salinity in the surface layers can vary over a wide range, as can be seen in Figures 4.3 and 4.4. The deep water masses by comparison have very narrow ranges for temperature and salt content and, whereas surface values change seasonally, the deep waters remain almost constant, at least on the scale of these diagrams: the values for the deep water shown in Figures 4.3 and 4.4 have not changed since first being recorded on the HMS *Challenger* expedition in 1873–75, although the instrumentation used then was more primitive and less accurate.

It is usual now to think of the ocean in terms of a '*two-box model*'; the surface layer and the deep layer, separated by the thermocline; in the polar regions these two divisions come together, but this two-box approach provides a useful way of dividing the description of the whole circulation of the oceans into two parts.

THE SURFACE CIRCULATION OF THE WORLD OCEANS

Surface Currents

Study of the surface circulation has given a basic picture of the major ocean currents as shown in Figure 4.6. With the exception of the Antarctic Circumpolar Current,

Fig. 4.6 The Major Surface Currents of the Oceans (in the Northern Hemisphere Summer, the circulation in the Northern Indian Ocean reverses direction)

which travels completely around the Antarctic Continent, the main features of the circulation in the three oceans are a series of current circles, called *gyres*. The major currents making up the circulation range from the fast, narrow currents crowded against the western edges of their respective oceans, known as the *Western Boundary Currents*, to the wide, shallow and slow *Eastern Boundary Currents*. The tropics have a complicated set of eastern and western currents running parallel to the equator.

It should be noted that, by convention, winds are named by the direction they come from, a south-west wind comes from the south-west. Current direction is specified from the direction the water is flowing. In addition, all the major currents are named, for example, the Gulf Stream or the Canaries Current.

Around the southern, open ends of the Pacific, Indian and Atlantic Oceans, in the region known as the *Southern Ocean*, the *Antarctic Circumpolar Current*, sometimes called the *West Wind Drift*, circulates eastwards around the Antarctic Continent. The boundaries are usually taken from *Sub-tropical Convergence* at about 40°S south to 60–65°S; this is shown in Figures 4.17 and 4.18. The winds circulate around the globe, driving the water, which is unimpeded by any land mass except the constriction of the Drake Passage between Antarctica and Cape Horn. These are the latitudes of the 'roaring forties', the 'howling fifties' and the 'screeching sixties'. 100 to $150 \times 10^6 \, \mathrm{m\,s^{-1}}$* of water are transported by this, the most massive of the world's currents, at velocities of 1 to 1.5 knots (0.5 to $0.75 \, \mathrm{m\,s^{-1}}$).

North of the Southern Ocean, anticlockwise current systems circulate in the South Atlantic, Indian and South Pacific. These are the *sub-tropical gyres*. The northerly flow towards the equator, the *Benguela Current*, the westwards Atlantic *South Equatorial Current* and the poleward *Brazil Current* make up the South Atlantic system with an offshoot of the Antarctic Circumpolar Current, the *Falklands Current*, travelling northwards along the coast of South America; in the Pacific, a similar system is the *Peru Current* (or *Humbolt Current*), the Pacific South Equatorial Current, then the *East Australia Current*. Both the Peru and Benguela Currents transport the low temperatures of the cold Southern Ocean waters towards the tropics, helping maintain the global heat balance. The Indian Ocean has the equatorwards *West Australia Current*, then the westwards Indian South Equatorial Current and finally the poleward *Agulhas Current*. All three of the polewards currents on the western boundaries of the three oceans are much faster and narrower than their counterparts on the eastern side.

The three South Equatorial Currents are more or less centred along the geographic equator. Beneath these, in all three oceans, is an *Equatorial Undercurrent*. This is likened to a thin ribbon of water; it is centred at about 100 metres in depth and flows eastward, closely tracking the equator. It may extend into the surface on the eastern edges of the oceans, but most of it remains subsurface so it is not shown on Figure 4.6, but it is part of the wind-driven surface circulation nonetheless, as it helps to maintain the balances in the equatorial transport systems. In the Pacific, it is known as the *Cromwell Current* after its discoverer, and carries some $25 \times 10^6 \, \mathrm{m^3\,s^{-1}}$ of water making it one of the larger currents in the surface system.

Along the Earth's *thermal equator*, which is on average, five degrees north of the geographic equator, is a region with light winds known as the *Doldrums* see Figure

*$10^6 \, \mathrm{m\,s^{-1}}$ is sometimes abbreviated to the non-SI unit, the Sverdrup, after the pioneering physical oceanographer, H.U. Sverdrup.

3.2; in all three oceans, an *Equatorial Counter Current* flows eastwards, north of the Southern Equatorial Currents.

North of the equatorial counter currents, gyre systems exist in each of the oceans. These rotate clockwise and are perhaps the best developed of all the oceanic gyres. The North Atlantic Ocean as the *Gulf Stream, North Atlantic Current*, (or *North Atlantic Drift*), *Canary Current* and finally the *North Equatorial Current*. The Pacific has the *Kuroshio*, the *North Pacific Current*, the *California Current* and the same North Equatorial Current as in the Atlantic. To put these currents into perspective, the Gulf Stream transports $55–65 \times 10^6\,\text{m}^3\,\text{s}^{-1}$ of water, at velocities of between one and three knots (0.5 to $1.50\,\text{ms}^{-1}$).

During the northern summer months, the Indian Ocean north of the Equator has a similar circulation, the *Somali Current*, the *South-West Monsoon Current* running into the South Equatorial Current. In the northern winter, this circulation reverses, the only one of the major current systems to do this, and the circulation described above rotates in an anticlockwise direction; the *North-East Monsoon Current* replacing the South-West Monsoon and the Somali Currents. The specific heat of land is much lower than of water. For the same solar radiation, land becomes hotter than sea. Thus the large land mass along the northern edge of the Indian Ocean draws in air off the ocean during the summer months as the land heats up and creates a low pressure zone; in the winter, the cold continent becomes a zone of cooling, descending air masses, a region of high pressure, and winds are blown off north-easterly across the ocean.

North of the Gulf Stream and Kuroshio systems, fitting into the remainder of the Atlantic and North Pacific Oceans, two further gyres can be seen. These are the *sub-polar gyres*. In the Atlantic, complicated by the geography of region, a gyre developed with the North Atlantic Current; the *Norwegian Current*, the *East Greenland Current*, the *Irminger Current* and the *Labrador Current* make up the counterclockwise circulation. In the North Pacific, a simpler system, made up from the North Pacific, the *Alaska Current*, and the southerly flowing *Oyashio Current* can easily be picked out on the current map at Figure 4.6. Again, the western boundary currents are the strongest.

Further north, the Arctic Ocean itself, while mostly covered by sea ice, still circulates with a wind-driven current. The ice-pack slowly revolves clockwise (when viewed from over the North Pole, this direction is also known as *anticyclonic*); the major inlet of water coming from the Norwegian Current and exiting with the East Greenland Current and the Labrador Current. There is some small inflow through the Bering Strait from the North Pacific.

The Coriolis Force and Ekman Transport

To account for these gyres and equatorial currents, in addition to the driving force of the wind, one must take into account the fact that the water motion is taking place on a rotating sphere, the Earth. All objects moving on the planet are influenced by the rotation of the globe, and are subject to the Coriolis Force, C_f (sometimes known as the Coriolis Effect or Acceleration). This is not a true force in the physical sense but results from the rotating frame of reference of the Earth; moving objects are deflected by it from their original straight track, turned to the right in the Northern

Hemisphere (and to the left in the Southern Hemisphere). The effect is most noticeable on moving objects loosely connected to the Earth, such as missiles or other projectiles, aircraft, ships, winds and ocean currents, which can respond easily to this sideways force.

Mathematically, the magnitude of the Coriolis Force on a moving object is given by the expression:

$$C_r = 2\omega \sin \phi v$$

where—

C_r is the Coriolis Force
ω is the angular rotation of the Earth, 7.292×10^{-5} radians per second
ϕ is the latitude of the object on the Earth
v is the velocity of the object

The Coriolis Force is then zero at the equator ($\sin \phi = 0$) (and zero, of course for an object at rest) and at a maximum at the poles ($\sin \phi = 1$). This is illustrated in Figure 4.7. This formula is for horizontal motion; there is a similar expression for vertical velocity, but as vertical water motion is very slow or negligible, it can be ignored.

Long-range gunnery has to take the Coriolis Force into account but consider here two slower objects latitude 45°N, first a ship moving at 10 knots ($\approx 5\,\mathrm{m\,s^{-1}}$). After one hour, steaming a straight course by rudder, the vessel would have been deflected 1.9 knots to the right of its track. This can easily be compensated when navigating the

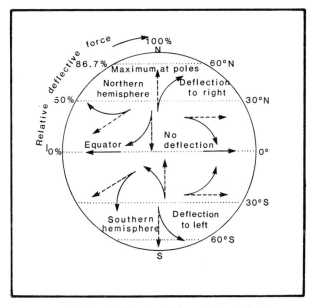

FIG. 4.7   Track of Moving Objects Deflected by the
Coriolis Force

ship, by steering a compass course; the required rudder offset needed to eliminate the Coriolis effect would hardly be noticed when the other deflecting forces such as wind, waves and ocean currents are considered.

An ocean current, with a slower velocity of one knot $(0.5\,\mathrm{m\,s^{-1}})$ would be deflected 0.2 knot to the right, 20 per cent of its distance travelled in the hour; without a rudder to hold the current on course, the water will be steered to the right, and if not constrained by other forces will spiral around in a circle. If surface water is given a push, perhaps from a storm of short duration, and after the wind has died away, the water will spiral around in the so-called *inertial current*, see Figure 4.8, friction eventually slowing and stopping the motion.

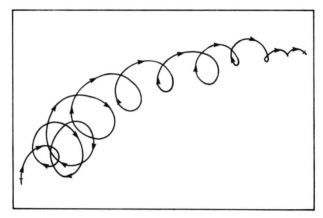

FIG. 4.8   Spiralling Path of an Inertial Current

These inertial current spirals rotate at periods governed by the equation:

$$T = 2\pi/f$$

where:

    T is the period,
    f is the Coriolis Parameter, $2\omega \sin \phi$

Thus the period is controlled only by the latitude, at the poles, T is approximately 12 hours, at 45 degrees it is 17.4 hours and at the equator, it becomes infinite ($\sin \phi = 0$).

It was noted in the last century that icebergs did not drift downwind as one might expect, bearing in mind their huge surface area above the water-line which should act like a sail. They moved at angles of 20 degrees to 40 degrees to the right of the wind direction. The physicist V W Ekman showed mathematically that when wind blew uniformly over the water surface, the immediate surface current should move at 45 degrees to the right of the wind direction (in the Northern Hemisphere), deflected of course, by the Coriolis Force. The surface current will be about two per cent of the speed of the wind (for a constant and uniform wind).

The water directly beneath the surface will also be set in motion, frictionally coupled to the first wind driven layer above. This second layer will move off, deflected to the right of the motion of the layer above, but with a slower velocity due to frictional losses. The third layer beneath will do likewise, and so on down the column. At a certain depth, the water will actually be moving in opposition to the wind direction; at this depth, the current velocity here will be about four per cent of the surface velocity and this depth, called the *depth of frictional influence*, is usually taken to be the limit of the wind-driven effects. This depth varies with the latitude and is typically between 100 to 200 metres. This whole phenomenon is known as the *Ekman Spiral* and is illustrated in Figure 4.9.

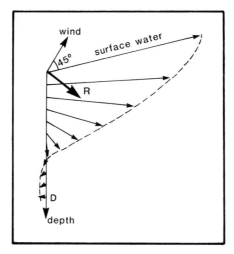

FIG. 4.9   The Ekman Spiral
Showing the Resultant Water Mass
Transport (R) Perpendicular to the
Wind Direction (Northern Hemisphere)

The Ekman Spiral has rarely been seen with the features of this diagram. The assumptions made in the mathematical model are never met in reality, the wind is never constant, the water may be too shallow for the full Spiral to develop, or the thermocline may inhibit the full effect in deep oceans. Nevertheless, the concept is important and accounts for the iceberg drift mentioned above. The iceberg, with most of its bulk underwater, responds to the direction of the currents, and it drifts at an angle to the wind direction.

There is also one important corollary. If the full Ekman Spiral is averaged mathematically, the result is the total water transport, sometimes known as the *Ekman Transport*. This is shown in Figure 4.9 and is at 90 degrees to the right (in the Northern Hemisphere and to the left in the Southern) of the wind direction. In other words, the wind-driven surface layer, averaged over the full depth affected, moves perpendicularly to the wind.

Using this Ekman Transport, the map of the generalised atmospheric winds at Figure 3.2, and the schematic map of a Northern Hemisphere Ocean at Figure 4.10, one can assess the effect of winds on the ocean surface. In the mid-latitudes, the

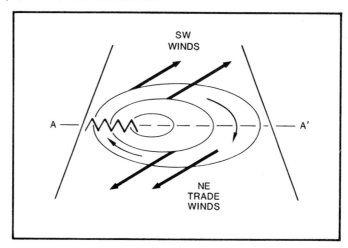

FIG. 4.10   Schematic Diagram of the Winds and Ocean
Circulation in a Northern Hemisphere Ocean

South-Westerly Winds drive the water south; the North-East Trade Winds to the south, push the surface waters north. The result is a hill of water in the region between the two wind systems. The situation to the north of the sub-tropical gyre is the reverse. The South-Westerlies push the waters away from the centre of the gyre, as do the Polar Easterlies. The result is a depression of the ocean surface corresponding to the location of the sub-polar gyres.

Gravity acts to restore equilibrium, water starts to run downwards, off the hill in the sub-tropical gyre, or into the depression of the sub-polar gyre. But this water is just another moving object, loosely coupled to the Earth, and is thus deflected to the right, to circulate clockwise around the hill, or anticlockwise around the northern depression.

This bringing together of water to form a hill is known as a *convergence* and, where water is removed from a region, *divergence*. This process accounts for much of the surface water movement. These hills or depressions of the surface are of the order of a few metres above or below the *geode*, the mean Earth's surface, and now can be measured directly by satellite radar altimeters (Chapter 5). The steeper the slope of the sea-surface, the faster the current velocity, and Figure 4.11 shows the topography of the sea-surface across the sub-tropical gyre of Figure 4.10. These are known as *geostrophic currents*, a term for water motion which is the result of the balance between the horizontal gradients and the Coriolis deflection. It accounts for the major surface current systems shown in Figure 4.6.

At the equator, where the Coriolis Force is zero (sin (ϕ) = 0) and there will consequently be no left or right deflection of moving water masses, the currents behave in response to the wind alone and run in straight lines parallel to the lines of latitude. Both the North and South Equatorial Currents pile water up at the western side of the oceans, and the Equatorial Counter Current flows back 'downhill' towards the east to restore hydrostatic equilibrium, the light opposing winds of the Doldrums having little effect.

If the Equatorial Undercurrents travelling eastwards along the equator veer away

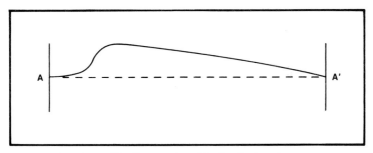

FIG. 4.11   The Topography of the Sea Surface Across a
Sub-Tropical Gyre (Line A-A', in Fig. 4.10)

from the equator, the Coriolis Force ceases to be zero and 'steers' the current back
on to course.

Westwards Intensification of Boundary Currents

Although the winds suggested in the schematic diagram, Figure 4.10, are supposed
uniform across the width of the ocean, the actual current gyres are not symmetrical.
The centre of the gyres, whether the flow is clockwise or anticlockwise, north or
south of the equator, is nearer the western side of the ocean. This effect can be
confirmed by examining the full surface pattern in Figure 4.6. This westwards shift is
again a result of the rotation of the planet and the Coriolis Force; remembering the
dependence of the force on latitude, (page 93), water moving polewards around a
gyre will experience a greater and greater deflection (sin (ϕ) increasing).

Conversely, currents moving towards the equator will experience less and less
deflection (sin (ϕ) decreasing). The gyre responds by accelerating the western
poleward currents and slowing the eastern equatorwards currents. This phenomenon
is generally known as *westwards intensification* and the western currents are the
Western Boundary Currents. To a first approximation, the gyres can be considered as
a closed-loop system, total water transport north and south in any gyre must be
equal. Thus the faster western currents will be deep and narrow; the Gulf Stream for
instance is less than 100 kilometres wide, up to 2,000 metres deep and travels at the
high velocities noted above, three knots ($1.5\,\mathrm{m\,s^{-1}}$) overall, although velocities
higher than this, up to six knots ($3.0\,\mathrm{m\,s^{-1}}$) have been recorded in the section of the
Gulf Stream known as the *Florida Current*.

The *Eastern Boundary Currents* are, by contrast, broad, shallow and slow. Widths
are of the order of 1,000 kilometres, depths up to 500 metres and speeds are usually
less than one knot ($0.5\,\mathrm{m\,s^{-1}}$). Profiles of these Eastern and Western Boundary
Currents are shown on Figure 4.11. As a corollary, the sub-tropical polewards
currents, the Gulf Stream and Kuroshio for instance, have less time to cool on their
passage and act to carry heat away from the equatorial and sub-tropical regions, to
the poles. Their eastern partners in the gyres, the Canary and California Currents, as
they are much slower have more time to come to thermal equilibrium at each latitude
as they progress southwards but still help in the global heat transport, removing cold
waters from the sub-polar regions.

THE DEEP CIRCULATION

Beneath the surface mixed-layer of Figure 4.5 lies the bulk of the ocean water mass. Although these waters are usually too deep for all but the deepest diving submarine, research submersibles and remotely operated unmanned craft, there are strong currents and large vertical motions. This section will review the circulation of the deep water, showing how it is driven and how it transports heat, salt and any other dissolved contaminant through the world ocean system.

Early theories of deep ocean circulation suggested that deep currents would be sluggish or non-existent, but the discovery of oxygen-consuming marine life on the abyssal plains, (by deep-sea dredging and recovery of submarine telephone cables) at depths of 4,000 metres, meant that, somehow, oxygen, dissolved in sea water, could reach these depths. The only source of this oxygen is the atmosphere and the absorption of atmospheric oxygen into the oceans can only occur through the sea surface. There must be some mechanism for the sinking of surface waters to replenish the oxygen in the deep waters.

Central to the study of deep circulation is the concept of the *water mass*. Water with a specific value of temperature and pressure is known as a *water type*. Examination of Figure 4.3 or Figure 4.4, shows that there are large volumes of deep ocean water with temperatures and salinities which only vary over a small range of water types. As an example, consider the water between three and four degrees C and salinity 34.9 to 35.0 in those two diagrams. This water occupies a major section of the North Atlantic Ocean, between 60° N and 30° S. This is a water mass, which is called the *North Atlantic Deep Water*, or as it is usually abbreviated, the NADW.

Using a graph with the vertical axis as temperature, and the horizontal axis as salinity, water types and water masses may be plotted; the result is the *T/S diagram*. This is illustrated on Figure 4.12 for an *oceanographic station* (a position where an oceanographic research vessel has measured the values of temperature, salinity and probably several other parameters) in the Mid-North Atlantic; the NADW is identified as the cluster of points around 3.5 degrees C and 34.9. In a similar fashion, T/S graphs can be constructed for all the oceans and one can identify other water masses. The major ones are the North Atlantic Deep Water, the *Antarctic Bottom Water* (AABW) and the *Indian* or *Pacific Common Water* (ICW and PCW). There are several other lesser water masses representing smaller proportions of the deep waters. These are the *Antarctic Intermediate Water* (AAIW), the Atlantic, Indian and Pacific *Central Waters*, the *Mediterranean Water* (MW), the *Red Sea Water*, the *North Atlantic Bottom Water* (NABW), and the *Antarctic Circumpolar Water*.

Not all of these water masses exist in every ocean of course; Figure 4.12 identifies the North Atlantic Central Water, the Mediterranean Water, North Atlantic Deep Water, and the Antarctic Bottom Water. The surface water will be off the graph to the right and is not considered here.

In addition to plotting the individual temperature and salinity points, one can also superimpose the lines of constant density, or *isopycnals* on to the T/S plot. These are given in an oceanographic parameter σ_t, called *sigma-t* and is obtained from a

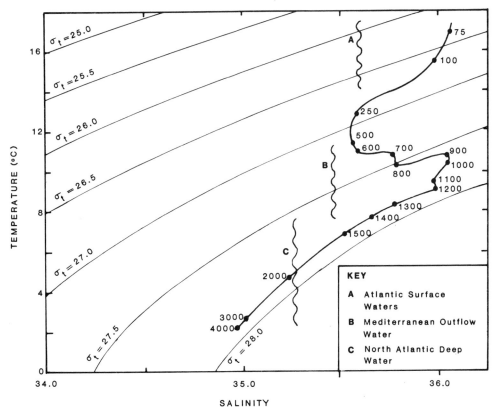

FIG. 4.12   A Typical T/S Diagram for a Mid-North Atlantic Station

formula which calculates the density of water from temperature and salinity values.*
The increase in density due to pressure is ignored in calculations of sigma-*t* as, to a
first approximation, water is incompressible.

Temperature and salinity are known as *conservative properties* of sea water. Once
out of contact with the atmosphere, these parameters can only be changed by
physical mixing with other water masses of different temperature and salinity. Thus
temperature alone, or salinity alone, can be used as an indicator of the presence of a
water mass if its mode of origin gives it distinctive values.

As an example, a higher than normal salinity found at 1,000 metres deep in the
North Atlantic indicates the presence of Mediterranean Water. This is a layer of high
salinity water which has flowed out of the Mediterranean through the Straits of

---

*The density of sea water is around $1,025 \times 10^3 \, \mathrm{kg \, m^{-3}}$. In most situations, the variations in sea water
density of any importance in oceanographic studies are less than 0.1%, and for convenience, the
parameter, sigma-*t*, is used which is defined as:

$$\sigma_t = \varrho - 1,000$$

In the example here, sigma-*t* would be 25.00. In studies of very deep water masses and their behaviour,
where the effect of compression on the temperature of water is important, the potential temperature is
sometimes used to calculate density and in this case the value is known as $\sigma\theta$ or *sigma-theta*.

Gibraltar as an *undercurrent* and spreads out as a distinctive layer in the North Atlantic Ocean; see Figure 4.13. Its origins are due to the high evaporation in the Mediterranean Sea itself, which increases the salinity, and of the cooling by the *Mistral Wind* off Europe; both increase the density of the surface waters. These sink into the deep and this saline water, being heavier than the waters in the North Atlantic outside, runs out of the Straits, flowing over the 350 metres deep sill at

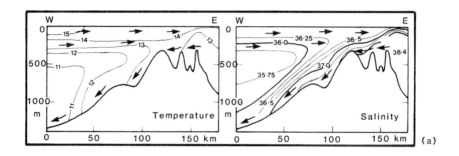

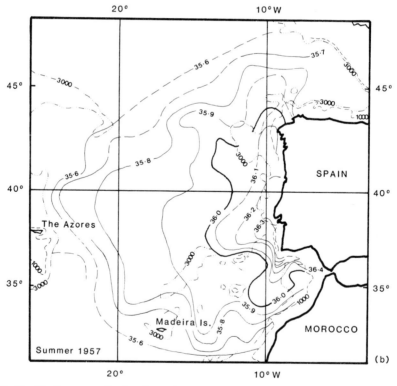

Fig. 4.13   The Mediterranean Outflow Layer in the North Atlantic Ocean Centred at a Depth of 1,000 metres. (a) The Outflow through the Straits of Gibraltar, (b) The Salinity of the Mediterranean Water in the North Atlantic Ocean

Gibraltar. To compensate for the outflow, a surface inflow brings Atlantic surface water into the Mediterranean to balance the water budget.

Once into the North Atlantic, this *Mediterranean Outflow* sinks and mixes with the existing waters at a core depth of 1,000 metres, spreading out horizontally, exchanging the excess salt with the waters above and below it. Using the salinity as an indicator, it has been traced across the ocean to the western side.[*]

Combining both temperature and salinity together on the T/S diagram shows the usefulness of both parameters used together as indicators. Additionally, the effect of mixing one water mass with another can be demonstrated and the characteristics of the resultant water mass calculated. Figure 4.14 shows how, if one begins with Water Mass A of temperature and salinity as shown and volume V_A and mixes this with Water Mass B of volume V_B the result is Water Mass C, whose temperature and salinity can be calculated from the relationship:

$$V_A/V_B = a/b$$

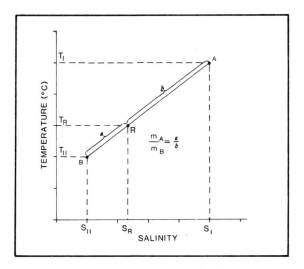

FIG. 4.14   A T/S Diagram showing how to calculate the temperature and salinity of a water mass which is a mixture of Water Masses A and B, with volumes V_A and V_B

The T/S diagram is a useful tool for analysing the mixing of water masses. It is not limited to analysing two water masses; Figure 4.15 shows how the Pacific and Indian Common Water, the water mass which makes up the bulk of the deep water in both oceans, can be seen to be a mixture of North Atlantic Deep Water, Antarctic Intermediate Water and Antarctic Bottom Water, in the proportions shown.

The technique also demonstrates the densities of the water masses involved. More energy is required to mix waters of different densities than to mix those of differing temperature and salinities but similar densities. Consequently, mixing of water

[*]A similar phenomenon occurs in the Indian Ocean. The Red Sea has a sub-surface, high salinity outflow through the Strait of Bab al Mandeb into the Indian Ocean at 1,000 metres.

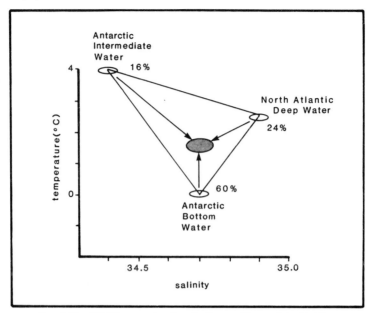

Fig. 4.15   T/S Diagram showing the Source Water of the Pacific
and Indian Common Water Masses

masses tends to be along the isopycnals, rather than across them. Figure 4.13 shows the Mediterranean Outflow inserting itself into the Atlantic water column above the North Atlantic Deep Water, despite its high salinity value.

Other tracers in the water can be used to track water mass movement and mixing; the Mediterranean Outflow has a distinctive low oxygen concentration due to its warm origins. Dissolved oxygen, however, is a *non-conservative* property of water, its concentration can be changed by mixing, but it can also be used up by marine life and in the decay of organic remains. Such non-conservative tracers are used with caution.

A problem with tracers is that they are not much help in establishing the rate of mixing. One modern tracer has helped here. *Tritium*, the *radioactive isotope* of hydrogen, was produced in great quantity during atmospheric nuclear weapons testing in the 1950s and 1960s. Rained out into the surface waters of the world's oceans, it can be used as a tracer; if one roughly knows the start time, it can help one keep track of the rate of mixing and spreading into the deep ocean.

The physical details of the mixing process are not well known beneath the sea surface. Probably turbulence generated by current shear where one water mass flows under another, the breaking of *internal waves* or the phenomenon of *double-diffusive mixing** all play a part in exchanging the properties of one water mass with another.

The motion of the deep water and this problem of the rates of mixing can be

*Double-diffusive mixing between two water masses relies on the fact that the molecular diffusivity of heat is 100 times that of salt. If heat diffuses out of a water mass faster than the salt, the water left behind, so-to-speak, will be heavier by virtue of its higher salinity, and will sink. *Salt fingers*, small columns of salty water falling from a layer above, can occur if the temperature and salinity conditions of the two water masses are correct to start with. This process acts as a mixing mechanism, distributing the heat and salinity of the two bodies of water.

examined with a variety of experimental techniques, deep-sea current meters and *Swallow Floats* which are buoys adjusted to float in mid-water and acoustically tracked, make direct measurements of flow. Photographs of the ocean bed can show ripple marks indicating strong bottom currents. Measurement of density gradients allows motion to be calculated in much the same fashion as measuring the isobars of the atmosphere allows one to determine wind strength.

These deep currents are slow, usually less than $0.1 \, \text{m s}^{-1}$; the strongest have been found on the western sides of the oceans, similar boundary currents to those of the surface circulation. Currents on the very bottom are controlled by the topography. The mid-ocean ridge usually isolates the western from the eastern halves of oceans, except where gaps and fissures permit flow, and several ridges isolate individual oceans one from another. A submarine ridge between Greenland, Iceland and Scotland keeps Arctic bottom waters out of the Atlantic; the sill under the Bering Strait effectively isolates the Arctic deep waters from the Pacific.

All the data can be compiled to present a picture of the three-dimensional movement of the deep water, the so-called *thermo-haline* circulation, the circulation driven by density differences between water masses.

Figure 4.16 shows a similar profile down the Atlantic Ocean as did Figures 4.3 and

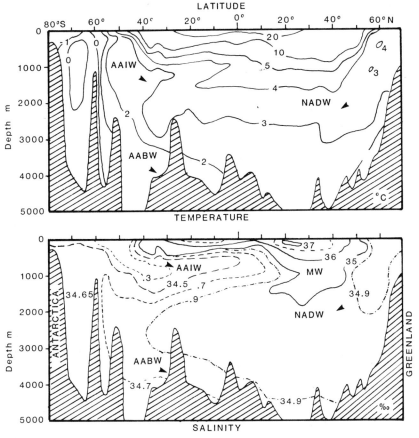

FIG. 4.16   Water Masses and Deep Circulation in the Atlantic Ocean

4.4, but here the water masses have been identified, together with their motion. The description starts with the Gulf Stream, part of the surface circulation (Figure 4.6). Warm water, made more saline by tropical evaporation, is carried by the North Atlantic Drift eastwards, and part of the current diverges northwards into the Norwegian and Greenland Seas. Here, intense surface cooling, especially in winter, causes the water to sink.

These cold, more saline, dense waters cascade out over the Greenland, Iceland, Scotland sill, whose average depth is 500 metres. The flow is thought to be intermittent, but large volumes pass across, mixing in water from above and below and increasing the volume of the flow as it passes into the main basin of the North Atlantic. This makes up the North Atlantic Deep Water, which progresses south-wards, tending to travel down the North American continental margin as a deep western boundary current. Under the NADW, a heavier water, the North West Atlantic Bottom Water sinks southwards as well, from its Labrador Sea origins mixed with Greenland Sea outflow, made heavier by the salt from the freezing of sea ice. When sea water freezes, salt is trapped within the ice, but, as explained in Chapter 2, the ice crystal rejects the salt and, over a period of a year or so, the ice discharges all the trapped salts back into the waters beneath.

The NADW continues on south, the upper layer receiving the influx of the Mediterranean Outflow as detailed previously. Still tending towards the western boundary, the NADW flows on until it reaches the Southern Ocean, where it becomes incorporated into the Antarctic Circumpolar Current, circling the con-tinent and flowing out northwards into the Pacific and Indian Oceans. The complex interactions of the water in the Southern Ocean is shown in Figure 4.17.

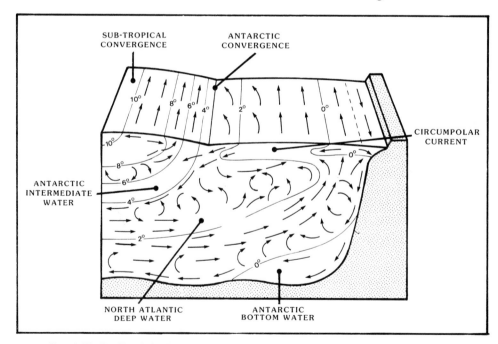

FIG. 4.17   Profile of the Water Masses in the South Atlantic Ocean and the Antarctic Circumpolar Current

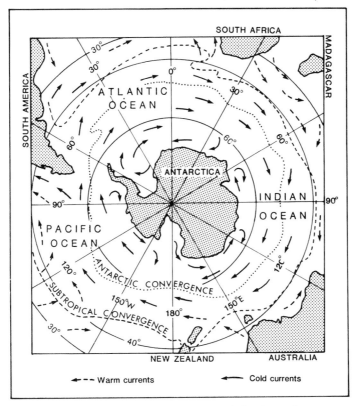

FIG. 4.18   The Surface Circulation of the Antarctic
Circumpolar Current, showing the Antarctic Convergence
and the Sub-Tropical Convergence

Above the NADW, surface cooling, this time in the Southern Polar latitudes around 50° S again causes sinking. Here, however, the salinity of this surface water is not high enough, even with the increase in density due to the lowered temperature, to sink the resulting water to the bottom. At this *Antarctic Convergence*, the water sinks back down to a depth of 1,000 metres and spreads northwards into all three oceans. The line of the Antarctic Convergence is shown around the continent in Figure 4.18, and the water mass produced is known as the *Antarctic Intermediate Water*. It can be traced back as a tongue of water, past the equator to about 20° N.

Part of the original North Atlantic Deep Water ends up in close proximity to the Antarctic continent itself, as part of the Circumpolar Current. Here, very intense cooling, and an increase in salinity due to sea ice formation, create the most dense of all the bottom waters of the oceans, the *Antarctic Bottom Water*, the AABW. Nothing obstructs its sinking off the continental shelf down into the floors of all the three ocean basins. Indeed the AABW is the most widespread of all the ocean water masses, and its production is estimated at $10 \times 10^6 \, m^3 \, s^{-1}$. By the time it has entrained water from above it into the flow, about twice that volume flows away from the Southern Ocean, underneath all the other water masses. The major source region is the Weddell Sea (Figure 4.18) where the water temperature is around −1.9 degrees C. In the flow northwards, it tends towards the western edge of each ocean; in the Atlantic, the AABW can be traced to 45° N, and in the Pacific, reaching the Aleutian Islands.

From this discussion, it can be seen that what started out as the deep circulation of the Atlantic Ocean alone, has broadened out to a description of the origins of the Indian and Pacific Oceans. There is considerable transport of polar waters across the equator, both southwards in the case of the North Atlantic Deep Water, and northwards, in the case of the Antarctic Bottom Water and the Indian and Pacific Bottom Waters. This is in contrast to the surface gyre circulation, where very little water crosses the equator. The deep waters are consequently an important method of heat transport, carrying cold waters to the tropics.

The origins of the deep water can thus be traced to two regions, the far North Atlantic and the Weddell Sea. No other region has the necessary climatic conditions to generate cold surface waters. From these sources, all the other deep water masses can be derived. Figure 4.15 showed the derivation of the Indian and Pacific Common Waters. There is no source of deep water in either of these two oceans. It is the 'end of the line' for the deep waters once they reach the deep Indian or Pacific basin.

In plan, the basic system is shown in Figure 4.19. This concept was due to the American oceanographer H Stommel in the 1950s and shows the deep western boundary flows.

These deep and bottom water production processes are more or less continuous. The question then arises, what is the eventual fate of the deep water in the Indian and Pacific Oceans? The answer is that they are slowly forced upwards, through the thermocline into the surface layers again. In addition, it is thought that some of the

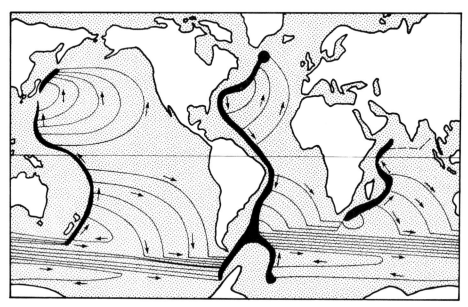

FIG. 4.19   The Model of the Deep Circulation of the Ocean, showing the Source Regions in the North Atlantic and Weddell Sea

NADW itself upwells in the Atlantic. This oceanic upwelling through the thermocline is slow. The water rises at the rate of a few metres per year at most; figures between 500 to 2,000 years have been suggested for the *residence time* of the waters in the deep box of our two-box system. Once back in the surface waters, it is into the gyres shown in Figure 4.6. Some might get back to the Weddell Sea or Norwegian Sea, cool and sink, starting the circuit again.

From the above, it is apparent that all the world's water masses are linked. A contaminant discharged into one water mass will eventually mix with all the rest, given enough time.

SMALL-SCALE PHENOMENA OF THE DEEP OCEAN CIRCULATION

The currents and movement of the major water masses as described in the previous sections, and shown in Figure 4.6 or Figure 4.16, are average descriptions, the results of studies taken over many years and by many methods. Calculation of the currents from ship drift observations in the early days of the sailing ship, messages in bottles (and more modern methods of using drifters, the satellite-tracked buoy), indirect methods which involve calculating the slopes of the density distributions of the surface waters, and direct methods of measuring current by using moored current meters, have all confirmed the general average picture.

Looking at specific regions in much greater detail has revealed that small-scale phenomena show much more variation. This study is sometimes termed *mesoscale oceanography* and the most important features to note, for the circulation in the deep ocean, are *fronts*, *mesoscale eddies*, Western Boundary Current *rings*, *internal waves* and *Langmuir Circulation*. The latter two phenomena can also occur in the shallower waters of the coastal shelves and seas.

Fronts

Although the previous sections might have left the impression that mixing between adjacent water masses is a smooth continuous process in space and time, there are many examples of where very dissimilar water masses co-exist side by side. These regions are known as *fronts*; six types of fronts are associated with the deep ocean and the large-scale circulation.

Planetary Fronts, divisions between different water masses extending over oceanic distances are the first of the oceanic fronts. These are usually found where wind-driven surface currents converge. The Antarctic Convergence, Figure 4.18, is a good example; it is sometimes called the *Polar Front Zone*. Across this boundary, the temperature jumps from values around one degree C in the cold Antarctic surface waters to six degrees C in the more northerly waters of subantarctic origin within a horizontal distance of 10 to 20 nautical miles. In the South Atlantic, the northerly waters have their origins in the North Atlantic Deep Water which is forced upwards as it approaches the Southern Ocean, Fig. 4.17.

The second type is known as a *Western Boundary Current Front* and these are associated with the strong currents which mark the western side of the oceanic gyres. The edge of Gulf Stream or the Kuroshio, for instance, are fronts of this type. Figure 4.20 shows a profile of the temperature across the Gulf Stream, showing the high

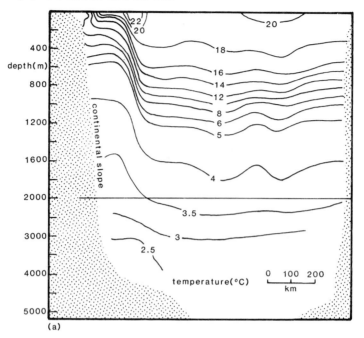

(a)

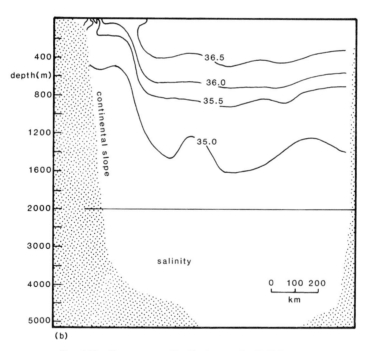

(b)

Fig. 4.20   Temperature Profile Across the Gulf Stream

temperature (and high salinity) waters of the Sargasso Sea to the left and the cold (lower salinity) waters of the North American Continental Shelf on the left. The front continues down to 2,000 metres deep, and these regions are characterised by high current shear, between the fast moving current and the slower waters on the edges.

The line between the two water masses of these oceanic fronts on the surface can be clearly seen on infra-red sensors carried by aircraft or satellites (or by making continuous temperature observations from ships). Visually, fronts are marked by lines of collected flotsam or disturbances in the wave patterns. Dynamically, they are characterised by intense friction, turbulence and vertical water motions. The marked horizontal contrast in temperatures, salinities and densities across these fronts allow severe distortion of sonar signals and complicate the problems of submarine detection which will be discussed in the next section.

There are four other types of fronts but as these are usually found in shallower coastal waters, they will be described in the following section. They are important in the interaction between the waters of the ocean and of the coastal seas.

Gulf Stream Rings

Rings, or Gulf Stream rings, are connected to the surface, wind-driven circulation and have radically altered the original conception of western boundary currents as well-defined, stable 'rivers of water' flowing through the oceans. Figure 4.21 shows the average or 'classical' picture of the Gulf Stream. Since the 1960s, the revised picture of the system is as shown in Figure 4.22.

The Gulf Stream was found to flow in large looping meanders generated by instabilities in the flow. The meanders could be pinched off to form rings in the

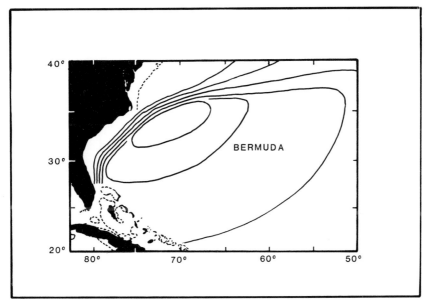

Fig. 4.21   The 'Classical' View of the Gulf Stream

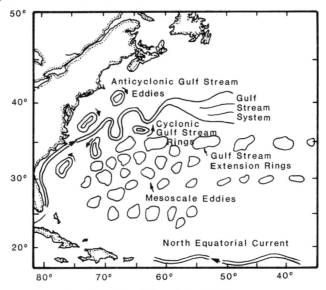

FIG. 4.22   The Modern View of the Gulf Stream System,
showing the Cold and Warm Core Rings

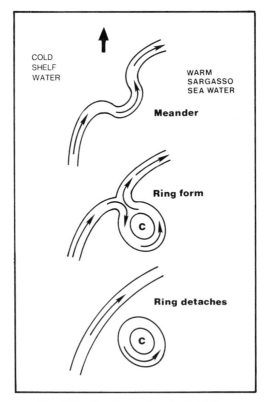

FIG. 4.23   The Generation of a Cold Core
Ring

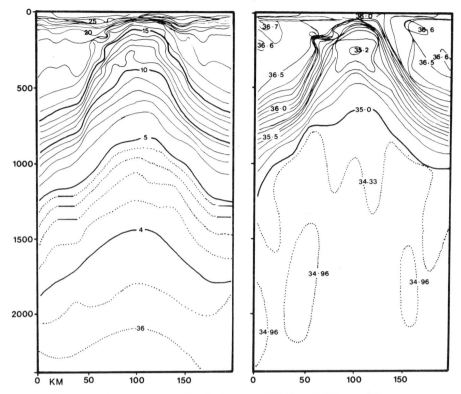

FIG. 4.24   Temperature Profile Across a Cold Core Gulf Stream Ring

manner suggested by Figure 4.23; a ring pinched off in the cold northerly waters has a warm core, and those pinched off to the south have cold cores. Figure 4.24 shows the temperature profile across a cold core ring. The rings are of the order of 10 to 200 kilometres in diameter, extending to 2,000 metres in depth and rotate at velocities of about $1 \, m \, s^{-1}$ at the surface of the core, with the rotation extending to the bottom of the ring. The cold core rings rotate anticlockwise in the Northern Hemisphere, and there is a depression of about 0.5 of a metre of the sea surface across the ring. Warm water rings rotate clockwise and raise the sea surface across the core.

The life cycle of a ring, once pinched out and set free to circulate independently, is to drift slowly southwards, on both sides of the Gulf Stream, slowing down, and finally coalescing back into the main Gulf Stream itself. Travelling with velocities of one to five nautical miles per day, this process may take one to two years, during which time they may be detected by their temperature anomalies with their surrounding water. Figure 4.24 shows a temperature profile through a cold core ring, showing the water temperatures usually associated with depths of 500 metres deeper found in the surface layers. Rings do not affect the net transport of ocean water because they are both generated and reabsorbed into these western boundary currents, but they have important functions in bringing water masses across the sharp front associated with these currents. Cold, nutrient-rich water is injected into the infertile Sargasso Sea region and warm waters are passed through the system to heat up the waters of the coastal region.

Rings, like fronts, are regions where the values of temperature and salinity change rapidly with both horizontal distance and with depth, causing distortion of sonar beams.

Meso-Scale Eddies

In the body of the ocean, large circulating eddies have been found. These *meso-scale eddies*, which may be associated with current systems, but are much slower than the true Gulf Stream ring, extend from the surface to the bottom of the ocean, a few hundred kilometres in width, with rotational velocities of the order of 0.1 m s^{-1}. These velocities are faster than the mean deep water flow. Meso-scale eddies have been compared to the atmospheric wind systems, rotating masses of air revolving around high or low pressure systems.

Little is known about these eddies and they do not exhibit the same sharp contrast in horizontal values of temperature and salinity as the Gulf Stream rings. With a large number of *synoptic observations*, data collected in different places all at the same instant in time, one can construct contour maps of the constant density surfaces in the deep ocean in the same fashion as the pressure charts of the atmosphere; the eddies show up as distortions of the isopycnal surfaces.

Internal Waves

Chapter 3 discussed the progressive, free surface wave. Waves can also exist and propagate along interfaces between waters of different densities. These are known as *internal waves*. A typical density interface might be the pycnocline, where light surface waters sit on top of denser layers beneath. In coastal situations, fresh water from rivers might lie on top of the heavier sea water as a distinct surface layer. (This example is often found in semi-enclosed *fjords* where tidal mixing is limited.)

Internal waves are illustrated in Figure 4.25, and they are propagated with a velocity given by:

$$c = (g h \ (\varrho_2 - \varrho_1)/\varrho_2)^{\frac{1}{2}}$$

where the symbols are as shown in the figure. g is the acceleration due to gravity, h_1 the depth of the upper water layer of density ϱ_1. h_2 is the depth of the lower layer of density ϱ_2 whose thickness must be greater than at least half the wave length of the internal waves.

Internal waves thus have velocities proportional to the difference between the densities of the two water layers. They are usually very slow in comparison to the free surface wave, of the order of 1.0 m s^{-1} or less, with periods ranging from tens of minutes to days. The small density differences usually seen between the two layers allow these waves to have amplitudes which can be measured in tens of metres, thus the effects of internal waves propagating below the surface can sometimes be seen on the surface, especially on calm days. Figure 4.26 shows an internal wave train; organic material collects in rows on the sea surface of the wave. This changes the surface tension and suppresses small waves. The result is a set of alternating bands of smooth and rippled water indicating the presence of an internal wave system

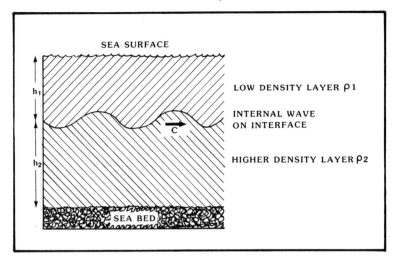

FIG. 4.25   Internal Waves on a Density Interface

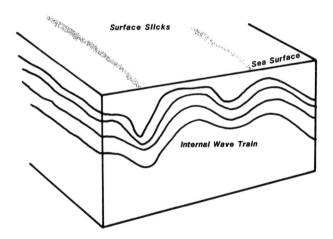

FIG. 4.26   An Internal Wave Train Near
the Surface

beneath. In fjords, the phenomenon of *dead water*, where small craft find difficulty making headway, is thought to be due to the excitation of an internal wave by the vessel which then impedes its forward progress.

The generation of internal waves may be due to a variety of causes—tidal currents flowing over bottom topographic features, atmospheric pressure systems or other short period wind stresses. It is debated as to whether submarines might also generate a train of internal waves which might persist for some hours. The density differences in the surface layers are more likely to support the internal wave, but as density increases all the way to the bottom of the ocean, there is no reason to suspect internal waves cannot be found throughout the body of the ocean. The waves act to distort the density surfaces and can affect sonar performance and may need to be taken into account in the ballasting of submerged submarines. Under certain conditions, internal waves can break as noted previously, just as their surface counterparts. In breaking, they help to mix water from the layer above, with the layer beneath.

Langmuir Circulation

A series of circulating cells can be set up by the wind. This system, illustrated in Figure 4.27, is known as *Langmuir Circulation* and generates the phenomenon of *windrows* over the ocean surface. These are long lines of particulate matter or oil films which collect on the convergence zones created by the helical currents converging on the surface. The long axes of the cells are parallel to the wind direction.

The spacing of the rows in the oceans is between two and 300 metres and the downwelling velocities could be one per cent of the wind speed, about 20–30 cm s^{-1}. The cells are rapidly set up with winds greater than 3 m s^{-1}, little is known about the

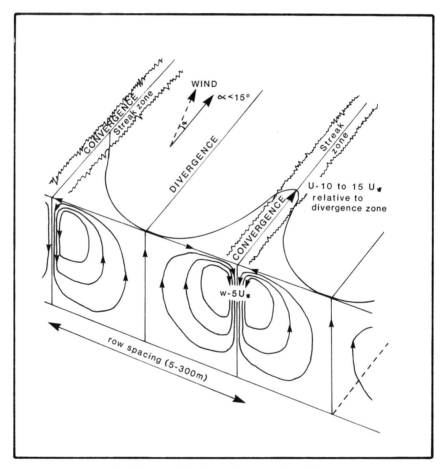

FIG. 4.27   The Structure of Langmuir Circulation

behaviour of the cells in strong winds. The depth of the circulation doesn't seem to extend much below seven metres.

Together with the mixing induced by the wind waves, the Langmuir Circulation helps mix the parameters of the surface waters, transporting heat downwards away from the surface, keeping the surface mixed layer uniform in temperature and salinity.

THE COASTAL SEAS

The deep ocean accounts for the global transport of heat using the major oceanic currents. The coastal seas are only a small part of the ocean, some four per cent of the total volume, and their shallow waters preclude them taking part in the major circulations. They are, however, the most important region for the interaction of man with the oceans. Fishing, coastal transport, mineral extraction and recreation all concentrate in the coastal zone. Most of the world's navies, moreover, have only coastal capabilities. The small-scale circulation and the water masses have implications for the users of these waters and for the tasks a maritime nation has to undertake.

The coastal region could be defined as the upper end of the continental slope and the continental shelf, see Figure 1.6 where the water depths would be 500 metres or less. The shelf itself averages less than 100 metres deep and, referring back to the chart, Figure 1.3, and the discussion in Chapter 1, it can be seen that some of these shelf seas can be very broad; for instance, the North Sea and Western Approaches, or very narrow, along the seismic margins such as the coasts of Peru and Chile.

On the seaward side, there are the large oceanic current systems shown in Figure 4.6. On the landward side, fresh, less dense, water is being discharged into the seas eventually to mix with the oceans, carrying whatever contaminant introduced by man into the marine system. In the coastal seas, various mechanisms operate, *upwelling*, *tides*, *estuarine circulations* and *long-shore currents* for instance. Several of the mixing processes contribute to the formation of the fronts associated with shallow seas.

Shelf Break Fronts

The boundary between the deep ocean and the coastal seas can be marked by changes in water characteristics. The coastal seas, especially those with large river discharges, tend to have lower salinities. With smaller volumes of water, temperatures can follow those of the adjoining land masses more closely. In winter, sea ice forms readily in bays where salinities are already low from river discharge. In summer, the flooding tide can cover areas of the *inter-tidal zone* which has been heated by the Sun, thus warming the incoming water. The deep ocean does not change temperature as rapidly as the shallower water and, as a result, a temperature front usually marks the edge of the coastal zone.

Upwelling

Certain sections of coastline are marked by a process which has an effect on the world

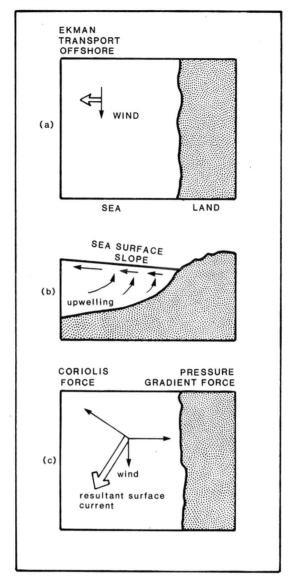

FIG. 4.28   (a) Wind Stress and the Resulting
Ekman Transport (b) Upwelling and (c) the
Resultant Surface Currents along Upwelling
Coasts

ocean transport model, and does interact with the offshore systems. These areas
have colder waters near the coast and are known as regions of *upwelling*.

Referring back to Figure 4.9, note that the net water transport due to a wind across
the surface of water is perpendicular and to the right (in the Northern Hemisphere)
of the wind direction. If local winds blow along the coastline as shown in Figure 4.28,
water is moved offshore. The water level along the coast is lower than out to sea. To
replace this deficit, water is pulled up from deeper layers, as shown in Figure 4.29.

This is upwelling and it is found in several areas around the world, the coasts of Peru and Chile, California, the Somali coast of Africa, the north-west coast of Africa and the west coast of India; all these regions have longshore local winds which blow in the correct direction for offshore transport.

The result is that cold waters from depths of 100 to 500 metres are brought to the surface, from bottom water on the continental shelf and partly down the continental rise. Figure 4.29 shows the isotherms associated with upwelling; this process brings water from below the pycnocline back up to the surface and acts, together with the much slower, global upwelling referred to on page 107, to return the deep water into the surface circulation. These upwelling regions are characterised by cooler climates, even though they may be in the tropics.

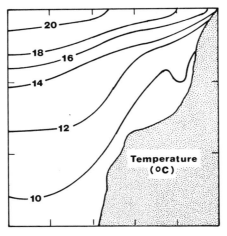

FIG. 4.29   Cold, Subsurface
Waters in Upwelling Regions

Of military importance, this system produces what is known as an *upwelling front*. The colder water contrasts with the warmer waters of the surrounding ocean. Figure 4.30 shows the colder waters off North-West Africa in April. The demarcation between the warm and the cold waters may be marked by a series of eddies and there are known to be deep, compensating currents flowing along the continental rise and longshore coastal currents driven by the dynamics of the process. From an economic view, these waters are the most prolific of all the oceanic regions.

Although the biology of the oceans is not of direct concern to this volume, it is appropriate to consider the general web of life in the oceans to account for the high productivity of upwelling zones and their economic importance. Figure 4.31 shows the general circulation of nutrients and solar energy in the marine environment. The dissolved nutrient chemicals, nitrates, phosphates and silicates are utilised by the microscopic plant life in the surface layers, the *phytoplankton*. This process can only occur in the sunlit surface waters, called the *photic zone*.

Zooplankton, the smallest of the animal life in the oceans, graze on the phytoplankton, and in turn are eaten by the larger fishes. The end result of all this production is the return of the nutrient chemicals back into their dissolved state in the *nutrient pool* of the ocean, by death and decay of their remains, the organic tissue and

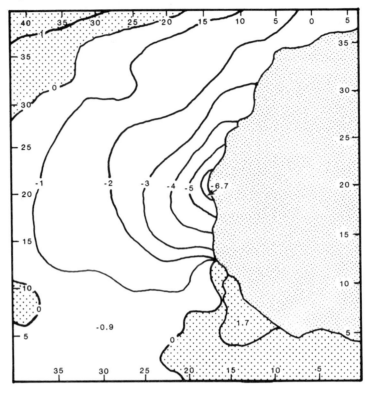

FIG. 4.30   The Difference between the Regional Average and the
Actual Sea Surface Temperature off North-West Africa in April

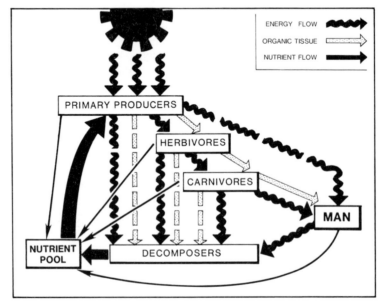

FIG. 4.31   The General Food Web of the Oceans, Showing the Flow
of Nutrient Chemicals through the System

faecal deposits. The problem is that these remains fall out of the surface layers, to deposits. The problem is that these remains fall out of the surface layers, to sink and collect on the ocean floor, where most of the decay and dissolution takes place. As Section 4.3 noted, the pycnocline acts as a barrier to upward transport of water, and of any dissolved chemicals. Without some return process, the surface waters would rapidly become depleted in the nutrient chemicals necessary to sustain the organic production.

Upwelling provides such a short circuit, and the chemicals which are released back into solution on the sea bed under areas of upwelling, are quickly brought back into the photic zone, to provide a continuing source of nutrients. These upwelling zones support very large fish populations which have great economic importance to the local economies. The most famous of these is the *anchovetta* of Peru and Chile. This is a small sardine-like fish which is caught and processed into fish protein; in the early 1970s one fifth of the world's yearly fish production came from these waters. Additionally, the anchovetta supports a large sea bird population, which in the past has provided a prolific source of agricultural fertiliser from their droppings, known as *guano*.

Periodically, however, resulting from climatic changes in the Western Equatorial Pacific, the wind system changes. Warmer water floods eastwards across the Pacific Ocean and spreads southwards down towards the Peruvian coastline, and upwelling ceases. This phenomenon, known as El Niño (The Child, because the troubles always seemed to occur at Christmas), causes mass mortality amongst the anchovetta whose food supply is curtailed and subsequently amongst the bird population. Death and decay in the water along the coastline uses up all the available oxygen and hydrogen sulphide gas is produced. Closely linked with the oceanographic changes, the atmospheric circulation alters and the whole American coastline of the Pacific is subjected to abnormal weather, with rains and floods. By contrast, the Asian and Australian continents suffer drought conditions.

The economic consequences for the South American fisheries dependent on the once abundant anchovetta are severe; the fish is used for animal feed stocks in the Western world, forming part of an interlocking chain of food resources. When this staple is not available, livestock farmers look for alternative supplies and the repercussions can affect the supply of basic human foods to poorer Third World countries.

After some months, the weather system re-establishes itself; upwelling resumes off South America, and if the anchovetta have not been too badly fished out, the industry can begin again fairly rapidly.

Tides

Although tides affect the motion of all the ocean waters, they are most evident in the motion of coastal seas. The regular rise and fall of the water level, and the strong currents which flow first in one direction, then some six hours later, reverse and flow in the opposite way are well known. Most coastal seas have *residual currents*; there is a net water movement after the movements due to the tide have been averaged out, but these residuals are usually very much slower than the tidal currents (sometimes known as *tidal streams*). Tidal water velocities in estuaries are of the order of 1 to 2 knots (0.5 to 1.0 m s^{-1}), but around headlands and other prominent features can reach 8 to 9 knots (4.0 to 4.5 m s^{-1}).

These tidal currents or streams play a large part in the mixing and scouring of the coastal seas, transporting river waters, the soluble river-borne contaminants, and the sands and other rock debris eroded from the land. The ultimate destination for these materials is the deep ocean, but the oscillating tidal flow works and reworks these particles before finally carrying them to the shelf break, where everything is transported into the abyssal plains by mud and turbidity flows.

Consequently, tides play a large part in shaping coastlines, building sand banks, scouring estuarine channels or silting up harbours. Some of the smaller ports are only navigable when the tide is high, others must resort to tidal docks. A deep-water port, usable at all states of the tide is an asset for naval operations; where this is not possible, vessels must either remain offshore at anchor, or be structurally capable of going aground when the tide falls. Julius Cæsar's ships in his invasion of Britain were lost because of ignorance of the tides.

In terms of height, tidal range can vary from a few centimetres, for instance southern Norway or the Mediterranean Sea, to three to five metres as an average, but tidal ranges as high as 15 metres are known in the Bay of Fundy in Canada.

The rise and fall of the tides are regular wave motions, and can be predicted. The *tidal day* is 24 hours 50 minutes long, and in this time most locations experience two high waters and two lows. This is known as a *semi-diurnal tide*; some regions, the Gulf of Mexico is a good example, only experience one high and low per day and these are known as *diurnal tides*. Figure 4.32 shows the changing height of water at a port with a semi-diurnal tide. Note that the curve is not symmetrical. Figure 4.33 shows the same tidal curve, but this time plotted for a 30 day period. The 14 day cycle between *spring tides*, where the tidal range is greatest, and *neap tides*, where the range is least, can clearly be seen.

The cause of the tide is the gravitational attraction of the Moon and Sun on the water. Using the Moon as an example, Figure 4.34 shows the gravitational attraction of the Moon on the near side of the Earth predominating to draw out a bulge of water. On the far side of the Earth, away from the Moon, the water is drawn out in a

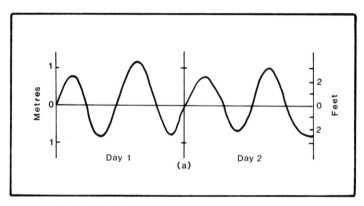

Fig. 4.32   A Semi-diurnal Tidal Height Curve for a Two Day Period

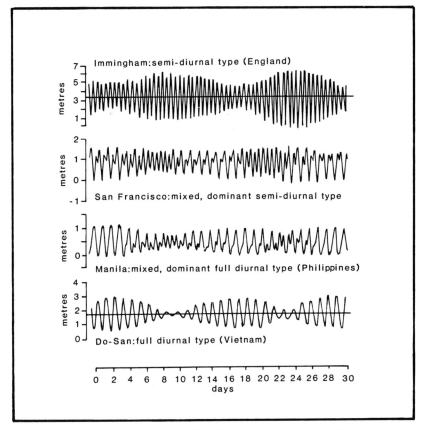

FIG. 4.33   A Semi-diurnal Tidal Height Curve for a 30 Day Period

similar bulge due to centrifugal force of the Earth and Moon system revolving around the centre of mass of the whole system. This representation is the so-called *Equilibrium Tide* and was originally formulated by Isaac Newton; it presumes that the Earth is smooth, without continents, and that the water can respond perfectly to the tide generating forces.

If one assumes the Earth now rotates under this water covering, it is easy to see how the land mass shown on Figure 4.34 will experience two high and two low tides per day. To explain the spring/neap cycle, the gravitational attraction of the Sun must be included. When the two celestial bodies act together as shown in Figure 4.35, spring tides result, when the Sun and Moon act at right angles, neap tides result.

The Equilibrium Theory explains the driving force behind the tides, but omits the north–south continents prohibiting the tide from travelling around the Earth, following the Moon. It is obvious that the theory must be modified. Additionally, the bulge of water revolving around the globe would imply speeds of $458\,\mathrm{m\,s}^{-1}$ at the equator. The water will act as a shallow water wave with velocity $c = (gh)^{\frac{1}{2}}$ (Chapter 3) and using appropriate depths, this implies a velocity of $200\,\mathrm{m\,s}^{-1}$. The tide obviously cannot act as a free water wave.

The *Dynamical Theory* used today treats the tide as a forced wave motion, and one

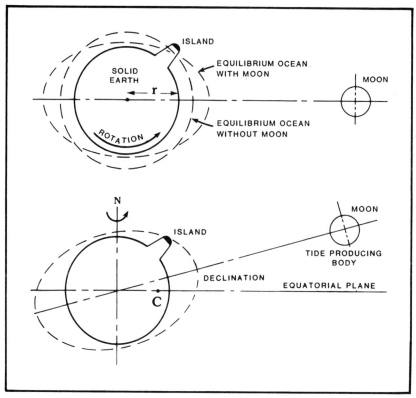

FIG. 4.34   The Equilibrium Tide. r = Earth radius, C = centre of mass of the
Earth/Moon system

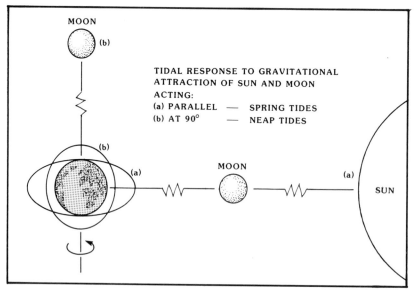

FIG. 4.35   Generation of Spring and Neap Tides using the Equilibrium
Theory of Tides

can use standard mathematical methods to analyse a tidal curve for the constituents of the wave motion. This is similar to examining the components of surface waves discussed in Chapter 3. Where the dimensions of the sea correspond closely to one of the forcing components or of a combination of components, the tidal response is amplified. The majority of coastlines respond to the semi-diurnal components, but the natural frequency for the water in the Gulf of Mexico, for instance, is about 24 hours and thus this region has a diurnal tide.

Tidal predictions can be made from analysis of tidal records collected by measurements in ports, and these are published by many authorities. Figure 4.36 shows a typical tide table entry for the port of Plymouth on the south coast of the United Kingdom. These predictions are accurate to within a few centimetres in height and a few minutes in time, remembering, however, that the other forces which may alter the water level, such as atmospheric pressure, winds or unusual fresh water river discharges, cannot be predicted by the tables and the actual level on the day may be somewhat different.

When the tidal heights for coasts are analysed, it is found that tides rotate around oceans and semi-enclosed seas. This phenomenon is due to the Coriolis Force continuously deflecting the tidal currents to the right in the Northern Hemisphere. Figure 4.38 shows how the times of *High Water*, the *co-tidal lines*, revolve around *amphidromic points* in the North Sea; at these points, there is no tidal rise and fall.

The average tidal range is shown by the *co-range lines*. The North Sea has three such points. The high water starts at the northern tip of Scotland, travels down the United Kingdom coast, across and up the North European coast before finishing in Norway. Similar charts can be drawn up for all the other coastal seas, and even for the deep oceans themselves, although the tides in the deep ocean are not as well understood as those in coastal waters.

It is worth noting that internal tides can exist in the body of the deep ocean, in the same fashion as the internal waves discussed earlier. These seem to be intermittent and may be generated by a variety of causes, for example the interaction of the surface tide on density interfaces, or the flow of water over the shelf break. The result is a raising and lowering of the isotherms with a tidal period.

Prediction of the tidal streams can also be drawn up to show the strength of the tidal currents. Measurement of water velocity at all states of the spring and neap tides are plotted on charts to aid the navigator. Figure 4.39 shows such a chart for the English Channel; the times are related to times of High Water in the port of Dover. These charts enable the navigator to predict the help (or hindrance) of the tidal currents during his proposed voyage.

It is these tidal currents which stir up the coastal seas, mixing the nutrients which have fallen to the bottom, back into the water column. An adequate supply of dissolved oxygen is maintained in the water to aid the decomposition and decay by the turbulence in the water. In the same fashion as the upwelling described in Figure 4.28 recycles the dissolved nutrients shown in Figure 4.31, these tidal waters are biologically highly productive. The food web is re-inforced by the continuous supply of organic remains which is swept off the adjacent land masses and down the rivers; these are utilised by the *filter-feeding* and *benthic feeding* fish and *invertebrates* the shelled species. Coastal seas support the major part of the fishing industry.

ENGLAND, SOUTH COAST - PLYMOUTH (DEVONPORT)

LAT 50°22'N   LONG 4°11'W

TIME ZONE GMT   TIMES AND HEIGHTS OF HIGH AND LOW WATERS   YEAR 1986

MAY

Day	TIME	M	Day	TIME	M
1 TH	0440 / 1109 / 1708 / 2333	1.8 / 4.2 / 2.1 / 4.4	**16** F	0344 / 0948 / 1559 / 2212	1.9 / 4.2 / 2.1 / 4.4
2 F	0602 / 1234 / 1837	2.0 / 4.1 / 2.2	**17** SA	0442 / 1052 / 1708 / 2319	2.1 / 4.1 / 2.3 / 4.4
3 SA	0102 / 0733 / 1405 / 2002	4.4 / 2.0 / 4.3 / 2.0	**18** SU	0601 / 1207 / 1835	2.1 / 4.2 / 2.2
4 SU	0225 / 0841 / 1510 / 2103	4.6 / 1.7 / 4.6 / 1.7	**19** M	0032 / 0724 / 1325 / 1955	4.5 / 1.9 / 4.4 / 1.9
5 M	0325 / 0932 / 1557 / 2151	4.8 / 1.4 / 4.9 / 1.4	**20** TU	0147 / 0833 / 1437 / 2059	4.8 / 1.5 / 4.8 / 1.5
6 TU	0409 / 1015 / 1635 / 2233	5.1 / 1.1 / 5.1 / 1.1	**21** W	0256 / 0931 / 1538 / 2155	5.1 / 1.2 / 5.1 / 1.2
7 W	0447 / 1054 / 1709 / 2312	5.2 / 1.0 / 5.2 / 1.0	**22** TH	0357 / 1024 / 1634 / 2248	5.3 / 0.9 / 5.3 / 0.9
8 TH	0520 / 1131 / 1741 / ● 2347	5.3 / 0.9 / 5.3 / 1.0	**23** F	0455 / 1114 / 1726 / ○ 2337	5.5 / 0.7 / 5.5 / 0.7
9 F	0553 / 1205 / 1812	5.3 / 0.9 / 5.3	**24** SA	0551 / 1202 / 1818	5.5 / 0.6 / 5.5
10 SA	0022 / 0625 / 1238 / 1842	1.0 / 5.2 / 1.0 / 5.3	**25** SU	0026 / 0646 / 1249 / 1908	0.6 / 5.4 / 0.7 / 5.5
11 SU	0054 / 0657 / 1309 / 1912	1.0 / 5.1 / 1.1 / 5.2	**26** M	0113 / 0738 / 1334 / 1956	0.6 / 5.3 / 0.9 / 5.4
12 M	0126 / 0729 / 1338 / 1941	1.2 / 4.9 / 1.3 / 5.0	**27** TU	0159 / 0828 / 1419 / 2043	0.8 / 5.1 / 1.1 / 5.2
13 TU	0157 / 0759 / 1407 / 2010	1.3 / 4.7 / 1.5 / 4.9	**28** W	0247 / 0916 / 1505 / 2129	1.0 / 4.8 / 1.4 / 5.0
14 W	0228 / 0828 / 1438 / 2040	1.5 / 4.5 / 1.7 / 4.7	**29** TH	0336 / 1005 / 1556 / 2219	1.3 / 4.6 / 1.7 / 4.8
15 TH	0302 / 0901 / 1512 / 2119	1.7 / 4.3 / 1.9 / 4.6	**30** F	0432 / 1059 / 1654 / 2315	1.6 / 4.4 / 1.9 / 4.6
			31 SA	0537 / 1201 / 1803	1.8 / 4.3 / 2.0

JUNE

Day	TIME	M	Day	TIME	M
1 SU	0019 / 0647 / 1309 / 1914	4.5 / 1.8 / 4.3 / 2.0	**16** M	0525 / 1127 / 1754 / 2348	1.8 / 4.5 / 2.0 / 4.7
2 M	0127 / 0752 / 1413 / 2016	4.6 / 1.7 / 4.5 / 1.8	**17** TU	0636 / 1238 / 1908	1.7 / 4.6 / 1.8
3 TU	0228 / 0846 / 1506 / 2109	4.7 / 1.5 / 4.7 / 1.6	**18** W	0100 / 0748 / 1352 / 2019	4.8 / 1.5 / 4.7 / 1.6
4 W	0319 / 0934 / 1549 / 2156	4.8 / 1.4 / 4.9 / 1.4	**19** TH	0215 / 0855 / 1502 / 2124	4.9 / 1.3 / 4.9 / 1.3
5 TH	0403 / 1018 / 1629 / 2239	5.0 / 1.2 / 5.1 / 1.3	**20** F	0327 / 0956 / 1606 / 2224	5.1 / 1.1 / 5.1 / 1.1
6 F	0444 / 1059 / 1708 / 2320	5.0 / 1.2 / 5.1 / 1.2	**21** SA	0434 / 1053 / 1706 / 2321	5.2 / 1.0 / 5.3 / 0.9
7 SA	0524 / 1138 / 1746 / ● 2358	5.0 / 1.1 / 5.2 / 1.2	**22** SU	0538 / 1146 / 1804	5.2 / 0.9 / 5.4
8 SU	0604 / 1215 / 1823	5.0 / 1.2 / 5.1	**23** M	0014 / 0638 / 1237 / 1901	0.7 / 5.2 / 0.8 / 5.4
9 M	0035 / 0643 / 1250 / 1858	1.2 / 4.9 / 1.3 / 5.1	**24** TU	0105 / 0734 / 1325 / 1952	0.7 / 5.1 / 0.9 / 5.4
10 TU	0110 / 0719 / 1323 / 1931	1.2 / 4.8 / 1.4 / 5.0	**25** W	0153 / 0825 / 1411 / 2039	0.7 / 5.0 / 1.0 / 5.3
11 W	0144 / 0751 / 1355 / 2000	1.3 / 4.7 / 1.5 / 4.9	**26** TH	0239 / 0910 / 1456 / 2121	0.9 / 4.9 / 1.2 / 5.2
12 TH	0217 / 0820 / 1428 / 2029	1.4 / 4.6 / 1.6 / 4.8	**27** F	0324 / 0950 / 1540 / 2200	1.1 / 4.8 / 1.4 / 5.0
13 F	0252 / 0852 / 1505 / 2103	1.5 / 4.5 / 1.7 / 4.8	**28** SA	0409 / 1030 / 1626 / 2240	1.4 / 4.6 / 1.6 / 4.8
14 SA	0333 / 0931 / 1549 / 2147	1.6 / 4.5 / 1.8 / 4.7	**29** SU	0458 / 1113 / 1717 / 2325	1.6 / 4.5 / 1.8 / 4.6
15 SU	0423 / 1023 / 1645 / 2243	1.7 / 4.4 / 1.9 / 4.7	**30** M	0551 / 1204 / 1815	1.8 / 4.4 / 2.0

JULY

Day	TIME	M	Day	TIME	M
1 TU	0019 / 0651 / 1304 / 1919	4.5 / 1.8 / 4.4 / 2.0	**16** W	0555 / 1156 / 1826	1.7 / 4.6 / 1.8
2 W	0123 / 0753 / 1408 / 2022	4.5 / 1.8 / 4.5 / 1.9	**17** TH	0023 / 0707 / 1313 / 1944	4.7 / 1.7 / 4.6 / 1.8
3 TH	0228 / 0852 / 1506 / 2121	4.5 / 1.7 / 4.7 / 1.7	**18** F	0146 / 0824 / 1435 / 2102	4.7 / 1.6 / 4.7 / 1.6
4 F	0326 / 0946 / 1557 / 2213	4.6 / 1.6 / 4.8 / 1.6	**19** SA	0313 / 0937 / 1551 / 2212	4.7 / 1.5 / 4.9 / 1.3
5 SA	0418 / 1034 / 1643 / 2259	4.7 / 1.4 / 4.9 / 1.4	**20** SU	0428 / 1041 / 1658 / 2313	4.9 / 1.2 / 5.1 / 1.0
6 SU	0505 / 1117 / 1727 / 2342 ○	4.8 / 1.4 / 5.0 / 1.3	**21** M	0534 / 1137 / 1759	5.0 / 1.0 / 5.3
7 M	0549 / 1157 / 1807	4.8 / 1.3 / 5.1	**22** TU	0007 / 0634 / 1228 / 1854	0.8 / 5.1 / 0.8 / 5.5
8 TU	0020 / 0630 / 1234 / 1844	1.2 / 4.8 / 1.3 / 5.1	**23** W	0056 / 0726 / 1315 / 1942	0.7 / 5.2 / 0.8 / 5.5
9 W	0056 / 0707 / 1309 / 1918	1.2 / 4.8 / 1.3 / 5.1	**24** TH	0141 / 0811 / 1357 / 2024	0.6 / 5.2 / 0.8 / 5.4
10 TH	0131 / 0740 / 1343 / 1948	1.2 / 4.8 / 1.3 / 5.1	**25** F	0222 / 0848 / 1436 / 2058	0.8 / 5.1 / 1.0 / 5.3
11 F	0205 / 0810 / 1418 / 2017	1.2 / 4.8 / 1.3 / 5.1	**26** SA	0259 / 0919 / 1513 / 2126	1.0 / 5.0 / 1.2 / 5.1
12 SA	0240 / 0840 / 1454 / 2047	1.2 / 4.8 / 1.4 / 5.0	**27** SU	0335 / 0947 / 1549 / 2153	1.2 / 4.8 / 1.4 / 4.9
13 SU	0319 / 0914 / 1535 / 2124	1.3 / 4.7 / 1.5 / 5.0	**28** M	0412 / 1018 / 1628 / 2228	1.5 / 4.7 / 1.7 / 4.7
14 M	0402 / 0957 / 1622 / 2212	1.4 / 4.7 / 1.6 / 4.9	**29** TU	0454 / 1100 / 1715 / 2317	1.7 / 4.5 / 2.0 / 4.5
15 TU	0454 / 1051 / 1718 / 2311	1.6 / 4.6 / 1.8 / 4.8	**30** W	0545 / 1148 / 1816	2.0 / 4.4 / 2.2
			31 TH	0023 / 0653 / 1312 / 1934	4.3 / 2.1 / 4.3 / 2.2

AUGUST

Day	TIME	M	Day	TIME	M
1 F	0144 / 0812 / 1428 / 2053	4.2 / 2.1 / 4.4 / 2.1	**16** SA	0138 / 0807 / 1427 / 2056	4.4 / 2.0 / 4.6 / 1.8
2 SA	0259 / 0921 / 1531 / 2154	4.3 / 1.9 / 4.6 / 1.8	**17** SU	0317 / 0930 / 1549 / 2209	4.5 / 1.7 / 4.9 / 1.4
3 SU	0359 / 1014 / 1622 / 2243	4.5 / 1.7 / 4.8 / 1.6	**18** M	0431 / 1034 / 1655 / 2307	4.8 / 1.3 / 5.2 / 1.0
4 M	0448 / 1059 / 1707 / 2324	4.6 / 1.5 / 5.0 / 1.4	**19** TU	0531 / 1127 / 1751 / 2356	5.0 / 1.0 / 5.4 / 0.7
5 TU	0531 / 1138 / 1747 / ●	4.8 / 1.3 / 5.1	**20** W	0623 / 1214 / 1840	5.3 / 0.8 / 5.6
6 W	0002 / 0610 / 1215 / 1824	1.2 / 4.9 / 1.2 / 5.2	**21** TH	0040 / 0707 / 1256 / 1922	0.6 / 5.4 / 0.7 / 5.6
7 TH	0037 / 0647 / 1251 / 1859	1.1 / 5.0 / 1.1 / 5.3	**22** F	0119 / 0744 / 1334 / 1955	0.6 / 5.4 / 0.7 / 5.6
8 F	0112 / 0722 / 1326 / 1932	1.0 / 5.1 / 1.0 / 5.3	**23** SA	0155 / 0814 / 1408 / 2021	0.7 / 5.3 / 0.9 / 5.4
9 SA	0147 / 0755 / 1401 / 2001	0.9 / 5.1 / 1.0 / 5.3	**24** SU	0227 / 0837 / 1439 / 2041	0.9 / 5.2 / 1.1 / 5.2
10 SU	0223 / 0824 / 1437 / 2030	1.0 / 5.1 / 1.1 / 5.3	**25** M	0257 / 0857 / 1509 / 2104	1.2 / 5.0 / 1.4 / 5.0
11 M	0300 / 0854 / 1515 / 2103	1.1 / 5.0 / 1.3 / 5.1	**26** TU	0326 / 0923 / 1541 / 2136	1.5 / 4.8 / 1.7 / 4.8
12 TU	0339 / 0929 / 1557 / 2144	1.3 / 4.9 / 1.5 / 4.9	**27** W	0400 / 1003 / 1620 / 2223	1.8 / 4.6 / 2.0 / 4.4
13 W	0424 / 1016 / 1648 / 2240	1.5 / 4.7 / 1.7 / 4.7	**28** TH	0443 / 1100 / 1714 / 2332	2.1 / 4.4 / 2.3 / 4.1
14 TH	0520 / 1121 / 1753 / 2356	1.8 / 4.5 / 1.9 / 4.5	**29** F	0547 / 1220 / 1841	2.4 / 4.2 / 2.5
15 F	0633 / 1247 / 1921	2.0 / 4.5 / 2.0	**30** SA	0104 / 0729 / 1349 / 2029	4.0 / 2.5 / 4.2 / 2.4
			31 SU	0233 / 0857 / 1502 / 2134	4.1 / 2.3 / 4.4 / 2.1

FIG. 4.36   Typical Tide Table Data for the Port of Plymouth (*Crown Copyright*)

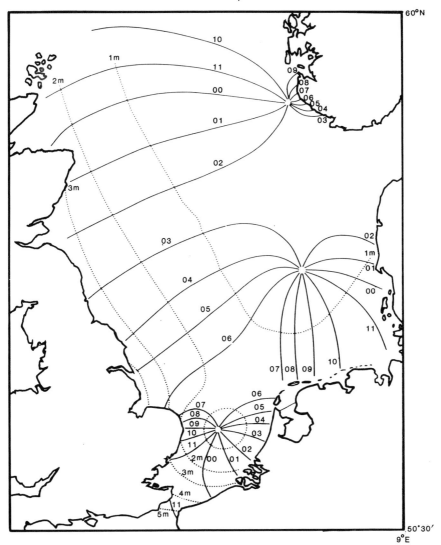

FIG. 4.37   The Amphidromic System of the North Sea, Showing the Co-tidal (times of High Water) and
Co-range Lines (average tidal range). Times are in lunar hours

Other Long Period Waves in Shallow Waters

Although not originating from the gravitational attraction of the Sun and Moon,
other waves appear in shallow waters. *Edge waves*, *seiches*, and *tsunamis* can change
sea level along the coastline in a periodic fashion.

Edge waves are controlled by the topography and 'trapped' along the coast; these
propagate down the coast in a fashion shown in Figure 4.39, with periods measured in
hours to days. There are *nearshore edge waves*, trapped by the beach topography,
shelf waves and *Kelvin waves*, trapped by the topography of the continental slope.
All of these waves act to raise and lower the water level, but because their origins are

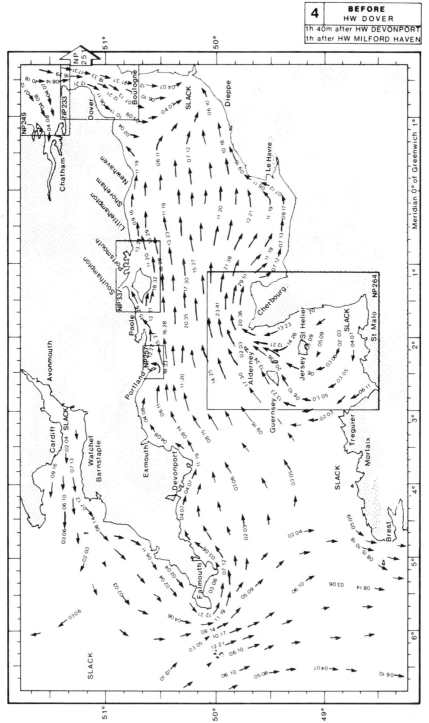

FIG. 4.38   Tidal Streams in the English Channel, six hours after High Water, Dover (*Crown Copyright*)

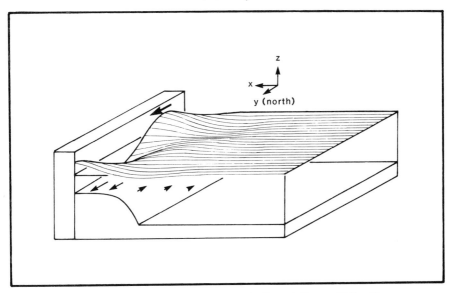

FIG. 4.39   General Schematic Diagram of a Coastal, Trapped Edge Wave

probably meteorological, born by events of large oceanic scale, prediction of their behaviour in the same way as normal tides is not possible.

Seiching, where the whole body of water in a semi-enclosed basin sloshes back and forth, is a *standing wave* and is often observed in lakes (and can easily be generated in one's bath!). A squall or gust of wind can set up the wave motion.

The amplitude of the seiche is of the order of a few centimetres; fjords and similar coastal embayments can seiche, the period of the wave can be calculated from:

$$T = 2L/(gh)^{\frac{1}{2}}$$

where T is the period of the seiche, L the length of the body of water, g the acceleration due to gravity and h is the water depth.

*Tsunamis** or *seismic sea waves*, are not generated by the tides although they have long been known as *tidal waves*. Large seismic events such as undersea volcanic eruptions or plate movements at destructive plate margins can generate a wave train which spreads out from the source.

They have wave lengths of the order of 100 kilometres or more and hence behave as shallow water waves, even across the deep ocean. From Table 3.2, and the equation shown on page 58, their speed is given by the shallow water wave equation, and velocities of $200\,\mathrm{m\,s^{-1}}$ (380 knots) can be expected across the abyssal plains.

In the deep ocean, such waves have amplitudes of a metre or so; hence they would not be detected by ships. When these waves reach a coastline, however, the wave height builds up. Sea level can rise over 30 metres as the wave approaches and this wall of water sweeps ashore causing great destruction. As might be expected, the Pacific Ocean, with its circumference of seismically active coastline, suffers most

*Tsunami means harbour or tidal wave in Japanese!

from this scourge. With a ring of *seismographs*, instruments for monitoring earth-quake activity, seismic events which occur underwater can now be monitored and warning issued to affected areas around the Pacific. As an example, a seismic event detected in the Aleutian Islands gives four hours warning to evacuate the population of the shoreline of the Hawaiian Islands. Ships in port need to steam rapidly out to sea, where the wave height will be lower.

Shallow Sea Fronts

Connected to the tidal streams, *shallow sea fronts* have been identified in coastal waters. These fronts mark the boundary between shallow, tidally-mixed waters and the deeper, more stratified waters further offshore. Schematically, these fronts are depicted in Figure 4.40, and a parameter S_H has been established which shows some success in predicting the position of these fronts.
    This is given by:

$$S_H = \log_{10}(H/U^3)$$

where:

   H is the water depth and U is the tidal stream velocity.

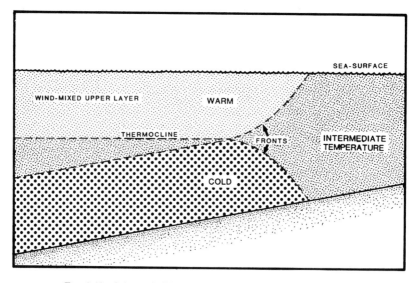

Fig. 4.40   Schematic Diagram Illustrating a Shallow Sea Front

    This parameter indicates the energy available from the tides to maintain a well-mixed condition. Where S_H is low, one finds these well-mixed water columns, and Figure 4.41 shows the contours of S_H for the United Kingdom coastline. Fronts have been observed by infra-red satellite images along the $S_H = 2$ contour (see Chapter 5).

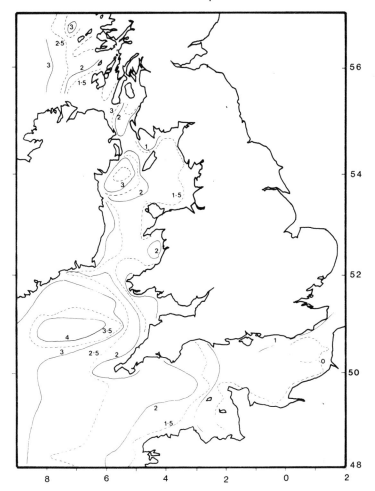

FIG. 4.41   Contours of the Stratification Parameter S_H. Shallow
Sea Fronts lie along the Contour $S_H = 2$

Near-Shore Oceanographic Processes

In addition to the tides and other wave phenomena along the coasts, oceanographic
conditions are also controlled by long-shore currents, local upwelling or river
discharges. The currents may be set up by wind conditions, by wind waves striking
the coastline at acute angles, or by density gradients induced by the supply of fresh,
lighter water. Along polar coasts, the situation is complicated by ice melt-water, or
the freezing of the sea ice itself.

Long-shore currents can be set up by onshore winds piling water up along the
coasts.* The result is a higher water level which, in flowing back down towards the
sea, is deflected to the right in the Northern Hemisphere, to flow along the coastline.

*In shallow water, the full Ekman Spiral (Figure 4.9) is not able to develop. Hence the net transport of
water is nearer the direction of the wind than the full ninety degree transport for deep water.

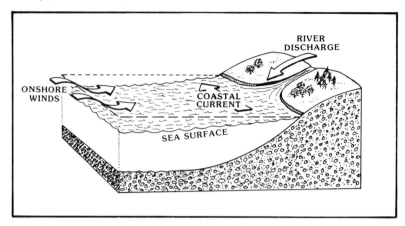

FIG. 4.42   Coastal Currents Generated by Onshore Winds or
Discharge of Fresh Water from Land Drainage

River or rain water can also build up a gradient of water along the coast which will produce the same sort of coastal current system. (Figure 4.42).

If this excess of water along the coast is created by abnormal storm wind conditions and if the high water coincides with a normal high spring tide, a *storm surge* can occur. The two high levels add together to produce a sea level higher than the normal coastal beach and sea defences and severe flooding can occur. This happened in the North Sea in 1953, and the low-lying countries around the southern perimeter of the sea have had to undertake large civil engineering works to build up defences against a repeat of the disaster.

Near the larger river mouths, the injection of less saline, hence less dense water into the coastal seas can create a *river plume front*. Especially for the larger rivers carrying a heavy load of sediments, the extent of the river influence can be seen for tens to hundreds of kilometres away, by the cloud of fine clays and silts in suspension. This plume can be carried down stream by the long-shore currents as shown in Figure 4.43.

Near to the mouths of rivers, one encounters *estuarine circulation*. *Estuaries*, the opening out of the mouth of a river into the sea, have a very distinctive circulation, driven by the flux of fresh water from the river itself, and by the constant ebb and flow of the tide. Estuaries are perhaps the most sensitive of all the oceanographic regions to pollution damage by man. Because of the supply of nutrients brought down by rivers, they are the most biologically productive regions on Earth per unit area; because of their sheltered, fertile lowlands and natural harbours, they were among the earliest regions settled by man. Now, most of the world's major cities are sited on or near an estuary. Consequently, the safe discharge of industrial and city wastes into estuaries is becoming an important subject for study.

Four types of estuarine circulation have been defined, the salt-wedge, the partially-mixed, the fjord and the hypersaline. Most estuaries are relatively new features geologically and were formed in the last ice age as discussed in Chapter 1, or in some cases, by tectonic activity, the movement of plates creating enclosed areas such as San Francisco Bay.

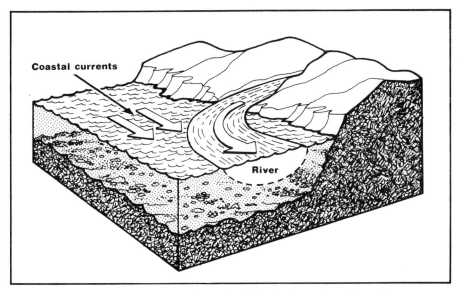

FIG. 4.43   A River Plume Front being Carried in the Long-shore Coastal Current

For the *salt-wedge estuary*, Figure 4.44(a), a layer of fresh water can be seen to lie on top of the more dense sea water; the wedge of sea water can be many tens of kilometres long. The energy of the river flow *entrains* sea water up from the lower layer, and this water is carried seaward in the upper layer. Thus there is flow seaward at the surface, but landward flow of sea water along the bottom, to replace the entrained volume. This circulation is a feature of rivers with large water flows, such as the Amazon or Mississippi, or where tides are very weak, such as in the estuaries of the Mediterranean Sea. For the very large rivers, this two-layer flow can be found well offshore.

For the *partially-mixed estuary*, tidal flow is of equal magnitude with river flow, and the whole salt-wedge is driven up and down the estuary with the rise and flow of the tide, Figure 4.44(b). There is no longer the sharp distinction between the surface and bottom waters, but a net bottom landward flow is still found, and the surface outflow is many times the volume of the original river discharge. These partially-mixed systems are the most common of the estuarine types and discharge of wastes into such systems must take into account this bottom return flow and the suspended material that might be carried with it.

The *fjord* or *sea loch* as it is sometimes called, has a circulation controlled by the *sill*, the submerged ridge found near the entrance to the open sea. Fjords can be very deep, of the order of hundreds of metres, while sill depths can be a few metres. This means that full tidal interchange with the coastal seas is impossible and flow is restricted to the uppermost layer, Figure 4.44(c). River water sits on the top and the bottom waters may remain trapped and stagnant in the fjord for many years before unusual storms or very high tides can inject cold, heavy, oceanic waters over the sill and renew the bottom waters.

The *hypersaline* estuary is rather rare, and occurs in hot climates where river flow is low, and evaporation high. There is a reverse circulation to the partially-mixed case;

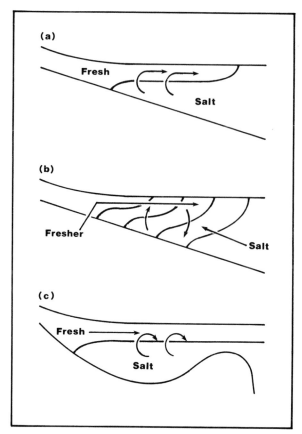

FIG. 4.44(a)   The Salt-Wedge Estuarine Circulation
(b)   The Partially-Mixed Estuarine Circulation
(c)   The Fjord Circulation

saline water formed in the estuarine flows out to sea along the bottom. Several estuaries in Australia and along the Gulf of Mexico exhibit this circulation, which bears some resemblance to the interaction between the Mediterranean Sea and the North Atlantic Ocean through the Straits of Gibraltar, as shown in Figure 4.13.

SOUND IN THE OCEAN

The problem is simple, submarines must detect other submarines or surface ships; surface ships must detect submarines. (A second problem is communicating with submerged submarines; here the same difficulties arise.)

Both *electromagnetic radiation* (radio, infra-red radiation, visible light, radar etc) and sound are wave motions and are used in air for detection and communication; light, however, or indeed any part of the electromagnetic spectrum, does not pass easily through water (although there is some experimental work with lasers in the blue-green part of the visible spectrum). Light of visible wavelength penetrates to depths of 200 metres in very clear sea water, but the presence of suspended material, plankton, organic debris, clays and silts cut this distance to fifteen metres in coastal waters. Radar, short wavelength electromagnetic radiation does not even penetrate the sea surface, ruling out this mode of submarine detection.

Sound, however, can be transmitted easily in water, and a method of echo-location using pulses of sound energy was tried out in the First World War to detect the presence of submarines. A pulse of high frequency sound waves (the 'ping') is generated underwater by a *transducer* and the echo received by a *hydrophone*. From the time of travel and knowing the velocity of sound in sea water the range and bearing of the target could be determined. This was known as *ASDIC* (Allied Submarine Devices Investigation Committee). The Second World War refined the technique, and the American term for the technique, *SONAR*, came to be used in preference.*

The basic electrical circuit to generate a pulse of sound waves is shown in Figure 4.45; the display might be a strip of recording paper, a cathode ray tube or a digital computer processor. The transducers can be made in a variety of ways, but *electrostrictive ceramics* made of barium titanate and lead zirconate are popular materials. Depending on the application, transducers can be used singly or in *arrays*.

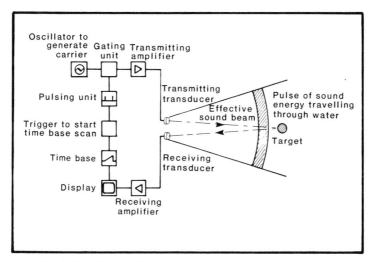

FIG. 4.45   Schematic Diagram for a Typical Pulsed Sonar System

It is not necessary to generate a pulse of sound, the so-called *active sonar* operation. Giving off a sonar signal betrays one's own position. Modern submarine systems rely more on listening to the sound of other warships to determine range and bearing and to identify the target, rather than pulsing and receiving echoes, much as humans do in hearing. This is *passive sonar*. All ships make distinctive noises and computer analysis of sound patterns is routine in target identification.

There are a number of uses for sound in the sea today, apart from the application in ASW. Sound waves can be used to pass information from ship to submersible or free diver in the same fashion as a radio link in air. Echo-sounding, as noted in Chapter 1,

---

*The term SONAR was a parallel to the name RADAR, and after being introduced was retrofitted to 'SOund NAvigation and Ranging'!

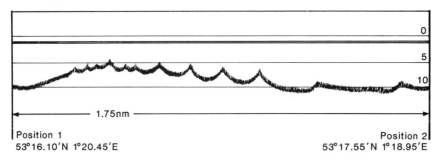

0
5
10

|← ————— 1.75nm —————→|

Position 1
53°16.10'N 1°20.45'E

Position 2
53°17.55'N 1°18.95'E

Echo sounder profile along south-eastern flank of CROMER KNOLL

FIG. 4.46   Echo-sounding Record of a Series of Sand Waves on the Continental Shelf

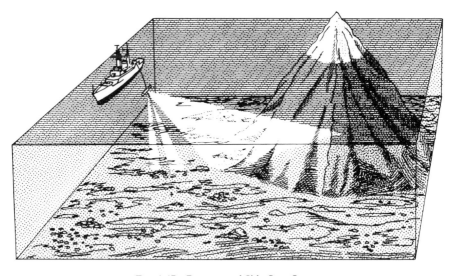

FIG. 4.47   Deep-towed Side-Scan Sonar

is used to determine the depths of the ocean, and a derivative of the simple beam of sonar, the *side-scan sonar*, can be used to illuminate the bottom, much as one might use a flashlight to scan a field at night. An echo-sounding record is shown in Figure 4.46, and a side-scan sonar display in Figure 4.47. A refinement of the echo-sounding system can be used for navigation; deep-sea drilling ships can maintain station in deep water, without anchors, by using a navigation system listening to a series of acoustic beacons positioned around the site of the sea bed.

One final use for sound waves in the marine sphere is worth noting. If an explosive sound source is used, as illustrated in Figure 4.48, the waves will take several routes to reach the receiving hydrophones. This is known as *seismic refraction surveying*, and can be used to determine the thickness of the geological layers under the sea floor; the oil industry make great use of this technique in offshore prospecting.

For all of the above, the behaviour of sound in the sea and how it is influenced by the water masses of the oceans is of great importance, and forms the subject for the remainder of this chapter.

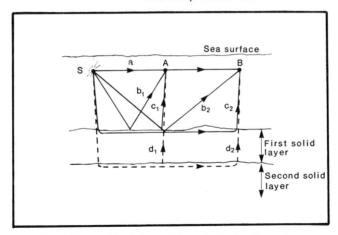

FIG. 4.48   The Principles of Seismic Refraction Surveying
using Sound. Analysis of Ray Paths a, b and c can determine
the type of sub-surface rocks

Propagation of Sound in the Ocean

Sound is a *longitudinal compression wave* and generates a changing *acoustic pressure* in the sea as it propagates. Except where it is constrained, by the sea surface or the sea bed, it spreads out with spherical symmetry from the source with a velocity given by the relationship:

$$c = (k/\varrho)^{\frac{1}{2}}$$

where c is the velocity, k is the *axial modulus* and ϱ the density of sea water.

The axial modulus is an expression of the elasticity or compressibility of sea water, and with the density, is a function of temperature, salinity and depth (that is, pressure). The mean velocity of sound in sea water is approximately $1,500 \, \mathrm{m \, s^{-1}}$; the frequencies of interest are between 30 hertz and 1.5 megahertz, with wave lengths between 50 metres and one millimetre.

By measurement of the three parameters, temperature, salinity and depth and substitution into an equation, the velocity of sound can be calculated. Velocity is found to depend directly on all three of the parameters; raising the temperature, salinity, or increasing the depth increases the sound velocity.

For a typical water column, such as was illustrated in the temperate location profile of Figure 4.1, the effect of the three components on the velocity are plotted in Figure 4.49. In the isothermal surface mixed layer, Region I on the figure, where temperature and salinity are almost constant, increasing depth increases the sound velocity. The presence of a seasonal thermocline in the surface water may alter the velocities at the top of Region I. Below, in Region II, the decrease in temperature through the thermocline lowers the velocity and there is a velocity minimum at the base of the thermocline. Beneath this, Region III, temperature stays almost constant, but the increasing depth increases the velocity. It can be seen that oceanic values of salinity variation do not play a significant role in altering the velocity.

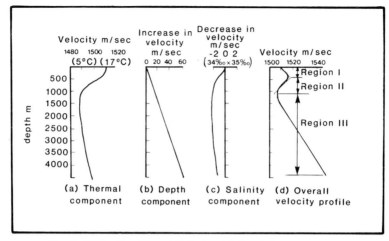

Fɪɢ. 4.49   Profile of Sound Velocity with Depth for a Temperate
Zone Water Column. Showing the Effect on Velocity for
Temperature and Salinity and Depth Changes

In spreading out from the transducer with this velocity *c*, the signal undergoes *transmission losses*. These losses are due to *spreading* and to *attenuation*.

In *spherical spreading* as happens to a sound source radiating in all directions, Figure 4.50(a), the intensity decreases as a function of the range only; this is the situation when the sound is trapped in a *sound channel*; losses are considerably less and hence for a given initial intensity, sound can travel much further in such a channel.

Sound is also attenuated by absorption of the sea water itself. The loss due to *viscosity* is frequency-dependent, the lower frequencies being less attenuated. This is

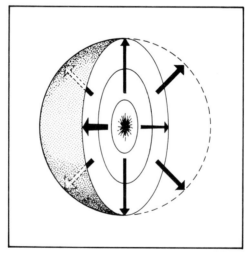

Fɪɢ. 4.50(a)   Spherical Spreading of a
Sonar Signal

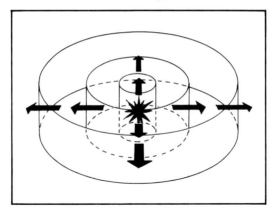

FIG. 4.50(b)   Cylindrical Spreading of a
Sonar Signal

shown in Figure 4.51 for fresh and saline water. The increase in attenuation at low frequencies is due to the presence of magnesium sulphate ($MgSO_4$) clusters in sea water, which selectively absorb the sonar signal. Boric acid ($B(OH)_3$) and scattering of the sound by suspended particles and air bubbles also attenuates very low frequency sonar signals.

Thus, for long-range transmission one would prefer a low frequency transmission. Losses are about five per cent per nautical mile at five kilohertz, as opposed to 90 per cent per nautical mile at 30 kilohertz. Low frequencies require larger transducers

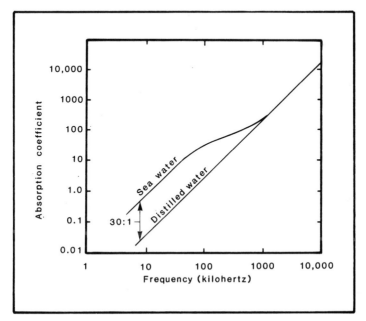

FIG. 4.51   The Attenuation of a Sonar Signal as a Function of
Frequency for Fresh and Sea Water

and higher power levels to operate, so the choice of frequency may be a compromise between various considerations including beam width and directivity of the signal. Where the target is small, in mine-hunting for instance, or in mapping sea bed features, high frequency, short wavelength operation is preferred as this is able to resolve the detail of the target better.

Having chosen the desired operating frequency, range should then be proportional to transducer power. High power pulse levels for active sonars, however, run into the problem of *reverberation*. The sea surface, air bubbles in the water, discontinuities between water masses, the sea bed and objects in the sea, from the small clay particles to schools of fish, scatter and reradiate a part of the sound pulse. These are considered as *volume, surface and bottom reverberation*. This effectively limits the system as unwanted signals arrive at the receiver together with the target signal. An example is given in Figure 4.52, showing strong bottom reverberation conflicting with the target signal.

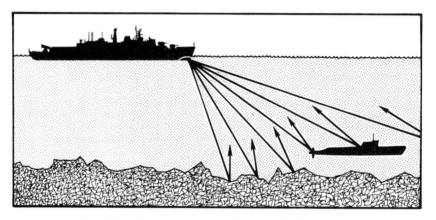

FIG. 4.52   Bottom Reverberation Obscuring the Target Signal

One particular form of *volume reverberation* has a specific biological origin. At depths of 180 metres at night, descending to 900 metres by day, a layer has been identified in most oceans. This *Deep Scattering Layer* (DSL) has been related to the daily migration of small organisms and perhaps their predators up to shallower waters at night, to descend again by day. The causes of this are not fully understood, but considerable signal strength is lost especially for downward-looking sonars at frequencies near 24 kilohertz. In the Arctic, the DSL lies just beneath the ice.

Reverberation and signal scattering is important in coastal seas. The sound is confined between the sea surface and the bottom and reflects back and forth between the two surfaces. It is found that rocky bottoms scatter the sonar signal better than sea beds of mud and clays and surface reverberation is known to depend on wind speed and sea state. Reverberation under ice also attenuates the sonar signal.

For passive, listening sonar operation, the *ambient* (or *background*) *noise level* in the ocean becomes important. The ocean contains numerous noise generators. Surface waves, turbulence in tidal currents, pack ice movement, falling rain and seismic disturbances are among the natural physical sources of interference. Many fish and invertebrates such as whales, porpoises, snapping shrimps and croakers add erratically to the general sound levels. Man-made noises, especially due to shipping in coastal seas, provide a continuous background of sound out of which the sonar operator must extract the signal of his target.

Ray Tracing

If the velocity of sound in the sea was constant, sonar would travel in a straight line from source to target (Figure 4.54(A)). As Figure 4.49 showed, velocity is not constant and changes with temperature, salinity and depth. Even in the well-mixed surface layer, the nearest to constant conditions possible, velocity increases with increasing depth. The concept of the sound *ray* is used to show the path the sonar signal will take as it travels through the complex structure of the ocean water masses. The ray is defined as the line drawn in the direction of propagation so that it is everywhere perpendicular to the wave front. Working out these paths, knowing the velocity profiles is called *ray tracing* and is usually done by computer.

The basic principle behind ray tracing is *Snell's Law*. When a wave crosses the *interface* between a fluid with one velocity into another with a different velocity, the wave is *refracted*; its path is bent. Figure 4.53(A) shows how sound waves are bent when the ray travels into deeper layers with increasing velocities; Figure 4.53(B) shows the situation when the ray travels into lower velocities. The wave is bent away from regions of higher velocity and towards regions of lower velocity. The actual relationship of Snell's Law is given by:

$$\cos \theta_1/c_1 = \cos \theta_2/c_2$$

where the angles θ are as shown in Figure 4.53 and c's are the velocities of the wave in layers 1 and 2.

If the beam is perpendicular to the interface between the fluids of different density, there is no refraction and the ray continues onward without changing direction. At a certain *critical angle*, the ray is totally reflected and travels along the interface shown in Figure 4.53(C). There will be some *reflection* of the ray at the interface; part of the wave energy will reflect back into the first layer, rather like a mirror. The sea surface also acts as a mirror to upward rays, and the sea bed reflects downgoing rays.

Figure 4.54 shows the behaviour of initially horizontal sonar rays in waters with different distributions of sound velocity. From sound velocity profiles, which vary with depth, one can consider the ocean to be a large number of thin, homogeneous layers, as in Figure 4.53; the resulting ray paths will be curved.

Figure 4.54(A) shows the nearest thing to a straight path. At short ranges, four to five nautical miles, sonar follows a more-or-less *direct path*. In Figure 4.54(B), sound will be bent downwards, away from the horizontal; this is Region II (from Figure 4.49). In Figure 4.54(C), with sound velocity increasing with depth as seen in Regions I and II, the rays are bent upwards. At the interface between Regions I and II, rays diverge upwards and downwards, and at the interface between Regions II and III, rays initially travelling upwards are bent back down and those travelling downwards are deflected upwards. Where the rays meet an interface at a suitable angle, reflection takes place and the sound wave can continue onwards.

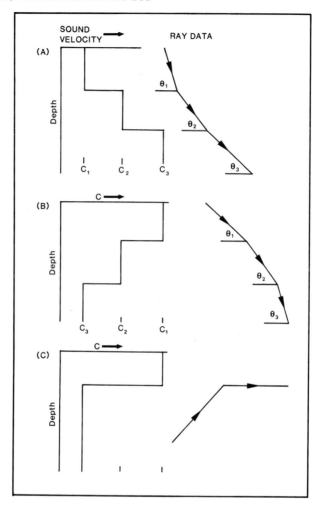

FIG. 4.53　Snell's Law Showing Refraction of a Ray
Path. (A) when the wave travels into a higher
velocity layer, $c_2 > c_1$ (B) when the wave travels into a
lower velocity layer, $c_2 < c_1$ (C) when a wave strikes
the interface at the critical angle

This behaviour shows the limitations in using sound for detection in the sea. Unless one is directly over (or underneath) the target, when there is no refraction, ray paths will be curved in the manner shown, there will always be *shadow zones* around the transmitter where no sound penetrates.* These shadow zones are indicated in Figure 4.54; their extent is a function of the vertical sound velocity profile and the depth of the transducer.

In the surface, Region I, sound is constrained to travel in this *surface duct*, leaving a shadow zone below the mixed layer. This zone will not be complete; sound leaks out of the surface layer by scattering from the rough sea surface. Internal waves can

*The ray paths in Figures 4.53 and 4.54 are reversible; if the transmitter was at the right of the diagram, the rays would take a reciprocal path travelling to the left.

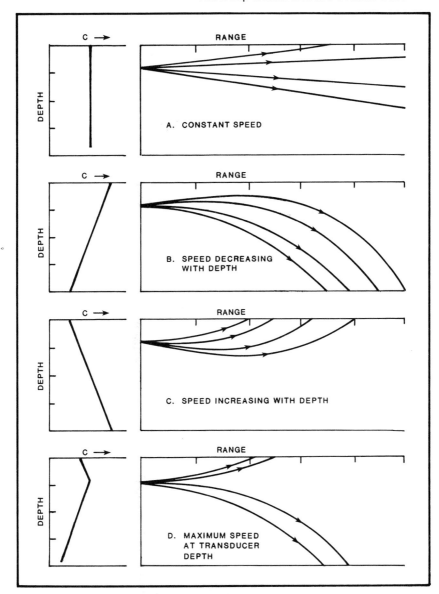

FIG. 4.54   Ray Paths from a Transducer Beam, for Sea Water with Different
Sound Velocity Profiles, Showing the Sound Shadows. (A) Constant Sound
Velocity (B) Sound Velocity Decreasing with Depth, Region II (C) Sound
Velocity Increasing with Depth, Regions I and II (D) Interface between
Regions I and II (E) Interface between Regions II and III, the SOFAR Channel

raise and lower the lower interface, changing transmission losses, and this
phenomenon shows the usefulness of using *variable-depth sonars*, which can be
lowered through the surface duct. This emphasises the importance of measuring the
sound velocity profile during ASW operations and of using several platforms to
search the area.

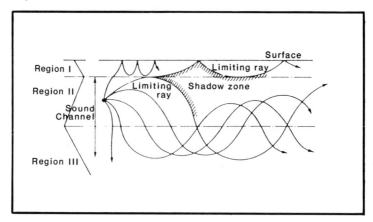

FIG. 4.55   Ray Paths for a Sonar Source in Region II, showing
the SOFAR Channel Effect

For sound sources below the surface duct, in Region II, Figure 4.55 is a combined diagram showing the ray paths. Sound is trapped in the so-called *Deep Sound Channel*, also known as the *SOFAR* Channel.* Sound energy is kept within this layer, centred at about 1,200 metres at mid-latitudes, and rising to the surface in polar regions. Cylindrical spreading applies here and, with little attenuation, sound can travel thousands of miles. Explosions set off in the North Atlantic Ocean can be heard in the Pacific. In theory, deep-diving submarines might be able to make use of this propagation; it is thought that whales communicate along the channel. The noise of shipping in coastal seas propagates down the continental shelf until it is trapped in the Deep Sound Channel, contributing to the background noise of the deep ocean.

Other transmission routes can be taken by the sonar ray. *Bottom Bounce* can be used for long-distance propagation in the deep ocean using sonars angled downwards, see Figure 4.56. This keeps the beam away from the surface ducts and allows long-range detection. Bottom bounce also occurs in shallow water, with multiple reflections between the sea surface and the sea bed. With the reverberations of the shallow seas, interpreting the signal is difficult under these conditions.

Where rays from a variety of paths come back to the surface together, they come from what is known as a *convergence zone* (distinct from the convergences of water mass mixing processes described previously). When the source is in the Deep Sound Channel, at about 35 nautical miles range, the rays converge on the surface, (and again at double the distance) as shown in Figure 4.57. The water depth must be great enough for down-going rays to be refracted upwards before striking the bottom, and therefore there is a minimum depth for convergence to occur. If the target is also in the channel, very long-range detection is possible.

Finally, all the above has been concerned with the vertical density, hence sound

*SOFAR stands for SOund Fixing And Ranging; it was thought possible to find downed aircrews in the oceans by detonating small explosives in the SOFAR Channel. The sound would be detected at shore-side listening stations, which could fix the crash position by triangulation. The phenomenon is sometimes used for missile-impact location.

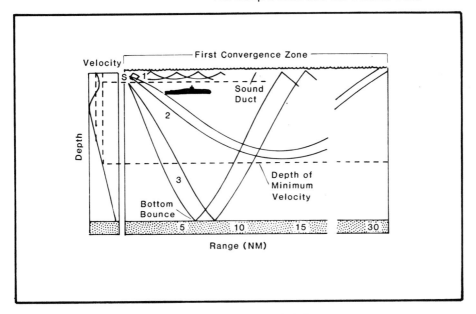

FIG. 4.56   Bottom Bounce Mode Sonar

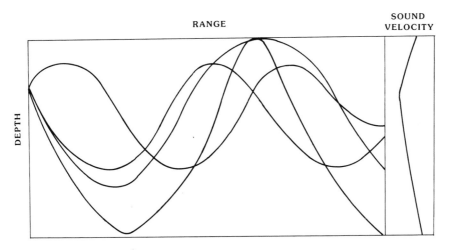

FIG. 4.57   First Convergence Zone for a Source in the Deep Sound Channel

velocity structure of the ocean. Earlier, it was noted that fronts between adjacent water masses also produce density discontinuities. These can refract the sonar beam, creating shadow zones. Referring back to Figure 4.20, the temperature profile across the Gulf Stream, Figure 4.58 shows schematically the ray path taken by a horizontal beam through the interface. Warm, less dense waters with high sound velocities are to the east of the cold waters on the west, and the beam is bent upwards. Fronts of all

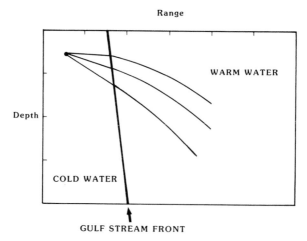

FIG. 4.58   Schematic of a Ray Path Passing
Through the Gulf Stream Front. Compare with
Figure 4.20

types, in shallow and deep waters, provide concealment and knowledge of their whereabouts is necessary for efficient anti-submarine warfare.

The oceans of the planet, together with their coastal seas, under the influence of the sun, the winds, tidal forces and the rotation of the Earth, form a complete system. There is constant exchange of water between the deep and the surface circulations in the oceans, and with the coastal seas and rivers. The behaviour of these water masses, how they are driven and the currents, fronts, eddies, waves and tides which result, form the basis for an understanding of the ocean's contribution to the world weather systems, for the productivity of the seas, for the transport of pollutants, and for the propagation of sonar signals. This understanding should be implicit in planning maritime commitments.

5

The Marine Environment: Present and Future

The years since the Second World War have seen an explosive advance in the scientific understanding of the sea, and in the uses man makes of the oceans. The traditional roles of transportation, fishing and warfare now number among a list which includes waste disposal, power-station cooling, tidal energy schemes, sea bed and sub-sea bed mineral extraction from the continental shelves, chemicals from sea water, recreation and the continuation of the age-old practice of smuggling, practised today with new and more dangerous substances than the traditional keg of brandy from France. By the end of the decade, the list may be augmented by wave and thermal energy plants, exploitation of deep ocean floor minerals and an expanded list of chemicals taken from the water itself.

Much of the above will be discussed in other volumes of the series, within the context of the vexed question of ownership of resources, and the role of navies and coastguards in protection, life-saving and crime prevention. Here, the intention is to discuss the way in which the marine environment responds to human demands, and the new ways of monitoring the health and behaviour of the oceans, with a time-span into the next century. The topics to be covered are monitoring, resources and pollution. All will require consideration by maritime planners.

MONITORING THE OCEAN

In Situ Observations

The traditional way of examining the details of the ocean, the currents, water masses, the chemistry, biology and geology is to go and have a look, take a sample or specimen, sometimes by remotely-controlled devices, and to bring these samples or observations back to laboratories for further examination.

Consider Figures 4.21 and 4.22 again. The 'classical' picture of the Gulf Stream system, Figure 4.21, was obtained from single observations by research ships, steaming along predetermined tracks, stopping now and then at an *oceanographic station* to take a *hydrographic bottle cast*. A dozen or so special water collection bottles with oceanographic *reversing thermometers*,* Figure 5.1, were attached to a

*The reversing thermometer is a mercury-in-glass instrument designed so that the warmer surface waters do not affect the colder readings of deep water temperature made by the thermometer as the bottles are pulled back aboard the ship.

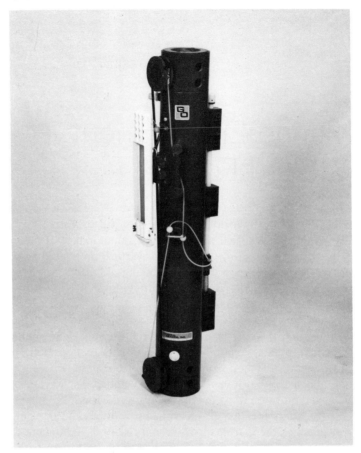

Fig. 5.1   The Water Bottle for Collecting Water Samples and
Measuring Deep Sea Temperatures (*General Oceanics—Sheba Associates*)

wire and lowered overboard. When the bottles reached the required depth, they
were triggered to close, trap a sample of water and record the temperature. The line
was pulled back on board and the water was taken off for analysis on the ship. The
whole procedure could take three or four hours for sampling deep water, which did
not include the time taken in chemical analysis.

It is apparent that collecting these observations takes a considerable amount of
time; ships must sail from station to station. Additionally, one only gets data at
widely-spaced points in the horizontal and in the vertical. Smooth curves must be
drawn for vertical profiles or contours of surface features. This latter point is well
illustrated in Figure 4.21. If Figure 4.22 is the 'real' picture, where must the ship
steam, to make the observations which will describe a transitory feature such as a
Gulf Stream Ring?

Part of the problem was solved by using electronic devices to record continuously
temperature, salinity (by measuring salt water conductivity) and depth. A device,
known as a *CTD Probe*, was lowered from the ship. A version is shown in Figure 5.2.
Similar devices could monitor surface waters pumped onboard continuously as the

FIG. 5.2   A Conductivity/Temperature/Depth (CTD) Probe (*E G & G Ocean Products USA*)

vessel travelled between stops. From the early days of temperature, salt content and pressure, progress is being made towards the automatic analysis for the other elements dissolved in sea water.

The detail in the vertical that these new probes revealed, tells much about the mixing mechanisms between water masses. Figure 5.3 illustrates the small-scale layering in the water column shown by one of these CTD probes. The old ideas of smooth curves (Figure 4.1 for instance) drawn between isolated water bottle observations has given way to studies of the *microstructure* of water masses and the mechanisms of mixing referred to in Chapter 4 are under analysis. The possibility, for instance, of detecting the wake of a submarine by examining the 'scar' in the water column where engine cooling water mixes in the wake is one possible ASW application of microstructure study.

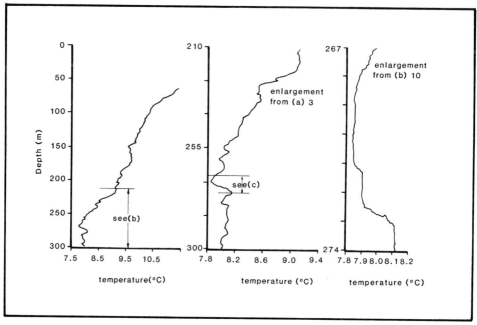

FIG. 5.3   Microstructure in the Water Column off the Coast of California. Note the enlargement of the profiles from (a) to (c)

In the same fashion, observations of current velocity can be made at fixed points. Figure 5.4 shows a recording current meter which measures the water's speed and direction, together with temperature and salinity. The meter is attached to a wire at the depth of interest, the rig is moored and the instrument records the data on an internal magnetic tape for periods up to six months. Deploying and mooring these meters is difficult and Figure 5.5 shows a typical current meter rig suspended from a sub-surface buoy.

This method of fixed point observations, as the water flows past, is known as an *Eulerian Measurement*. The problem is that one does not know what the water is doing somewhere else, at the same time. The solution would be to deploy two or more rigs. The cost escalates. An alternative is the *Lagrangian Technique*. Here one

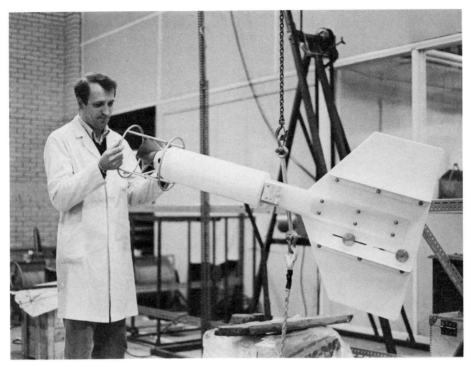

FIG. 5.4   A Deep Sea Recording Current Meter (*NBA Controls Ltd*)

allows an object to drift freely, either following the path taken, or more simply, by knowing the start and stop data, the probable course of the surface current can be estimated. The message in the bottle is the classic example of this latter method. A better device is a small plastic card which is not affected by the wind.

Tracking a drifting buoy can be done by following it with a ship, which, again, is expensive. A better alternative is to track the progress of suitably equipped buoys by a satellite link. This can eliminate expensive ship time, but each buoy still only describes the track of one patch of water. A derivation of this allows one to track deep water motion. A *Swallow or Mid-Water Float*, which is ballasted to sink to a preset depth, drifts in the deep currents and is tracked acoustically. The SOFAR Channel is useful here as it allows very long tracking distances.

The complete array of methods for examining ocean circulation is pictured in Figure 5.5. It will be appreciated that better results can be obtained using arrays of instrumentation, and several surface ships working in concert. This is the trend for modern large-scale oceanographic experiments and co-operation between ships and scientists of interested countries is necessary. A dense grid of data collection platforms, recording *synoptically*, is needed to resolve the details of phenomena such as Gulf Stream Rings, Mesoscale Eddies or the dynamics of the Western Boundary currents. The Intergovernmental Oceanographic Commission (IOC) of the United Nations have sponsored many such co-operative studies and the international exchange of data.

There is also a growing trend to install oceanographic data buoys, see Figure 5.6.

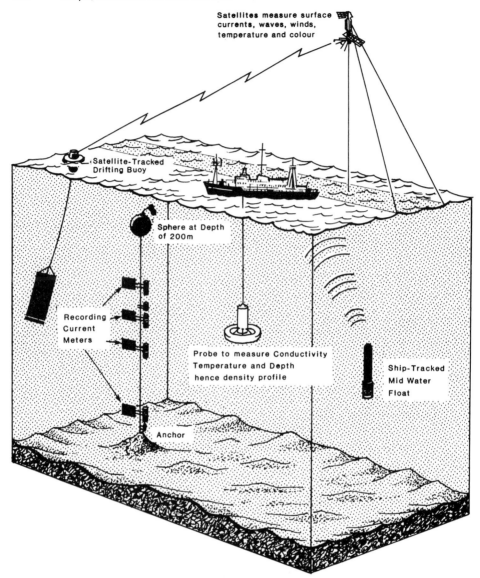

FIG. 5.5   Modern Methods for Measuring Ocean Circulation

To some extent, these take the place of *weather ships*, reporting back the meteorological conditions, wave height and period, temperature, salinity and the prevailing currents in the area. The cost of using ships is a major factor hastening the development of automatic data collection, although, especially in coastal studies, unmanned oceanographic instrumentation suffers considerably from damage and theft.

FIG. 5.6   An Oceanographic Data Buoy (*Thorn EMI*)

Remote, Space-borne Sensors

Even with multiple-ship studies, the methods outlined still only examine the conditions in a limited region of the ocean. The data must be added together to obtain the complete picture. Therefore, the trend has been to use techniques which scan large areas of ocean using the electromagnetic sensors of various wave lengths. The scanning platform could be an aircraft, and radars are mounted on cliffs to obtain inshore coastal wave and current data, but the future looks towards the environmental surveillance satellite.

Ocean temperatures can be scanned by *infra-red* (*IR*) sensors. The *National Oceanic and Atmospheric Administration* (*NOAA*) of the United States of America has sponsored a series of TIROS satellites which can resolve ocean surface temperatures to an accuracy of half a degree Celsius within a one kilometre square. Such observations, see Figure 5.7, show the warm (dark shades) and the cold (light shades) waters in the Western Approaches, to the south-west of the United Kingdom. Compare this to the theoretical picture for the fronts in Figure 4.41.

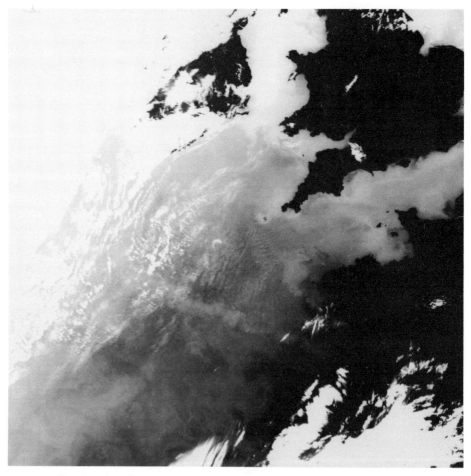

FIG. 5.7   Infra-Red Image of the Western Approaches. Warm water is dark
(*University of Dundee*)

Aircraft-based infra-red systems have detected ships' wakes, but whether space-borne IR sensors are suitable for this purpose has not been published.

It might be thought that the ice packs of the polar seas could be detected by infra-red scanners. It turns out that it is normally cloudy near the sea-ice boundary, and the polar regions are dark for half the year. This is a major disadvantage in using visible or infra-red measurements. Better success was found using microwave detectors which penetrate clouds and work at night; and sea-ice cover has been monitored continually since 1974. Using similar photographic techniques, notably those employed by the Coastal Zone Colour Scanner (CZCS) carried aboard the NIM-BUS-7 satellite, plankton density, and hence the biological productivity of the seas can be assessed using chlorophyll-sensitive wave lengths.

SEASAT

The first (and as yet the only) dedicated oceanographic satellite, *SEASAT* was launched in 1978, see Figure 5.8. Despite its short, three and a half month life, the sensors carried onboard have carried space sensing a major step forward. The results

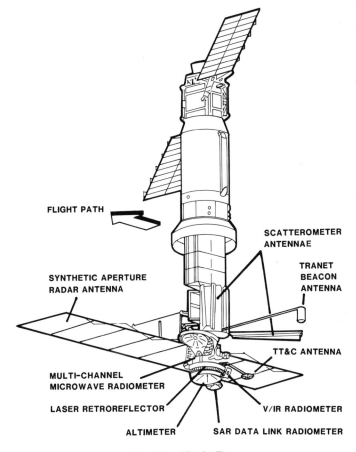

FIG. 5.8   SEASAT

and implications for future environmental space missions are still being assimilated by the scientific community.

A *radar altimeter* measured the exact height of the ocean's surface. This showed the gravitational attraction of the sea bed topography on the sea surface. (Refer back to Figure 1.2.) It is therefore possible to draw in some of the detail in bottom topographical maps, in the same fashion as Figure 1.3, without the use of echo-sounding data covering all sectors of the ocean. There is still the problem of resolving the exact water depth from the altimeter data, but the coverage by SEASAT has suggested areas of geophysical interest. The tides and major currents also affect the sea surface topography, see Figure 4.11; these slopes can be resolved from the altimeter data. Knowing the surface slopes, the magnitudes of the currents can, in theory, be calculated.

A radar *scatterometer* measured the *backscatter* of radar from wind waves on the sea surface. This determined the wind speed and direction, and the radar altimeter could be used to examine the surface waves themselves. It was fortuitous that a parallel experiment, *JASIN*, (standing for the *Joint Air-Sea Interaction* experiment), with several countries including the USA and the USSR and organised by United Kingdom scientists, was examining air-sea dynamics in the North East Atlantic. The data they collected was used to verify the radar data from *SEASAT*. It is always necessary to obtain what is called '*sea truth*', when using remote sensors.

The *swath width* of the altimeter would appear to be too wide for small-scale ASW searches, but the scatterometer work showed that satellite radar data could be used instead of surface ships, to gather wind and sea state information. Choosing courses for merchant ships to avoid extreme conditions while on passage, known as *weather routing*, is one possibility for this technique.

One other sensor carried on SEASAT was to generate great interest for future work. Up to now, the discussion has been centred on surface phenomena. Radar, although it works day or night, in rain or cloudy conditions, does not penetrate the sea surface. It would be useful to be able to examine phenomena below the surface. A *Synthetic Aperture Radar (SAR)* generated pictures of the sea surface resembling photographs. With suitable computer processing of the images, sea waves could be seen, as shown in Figure 5.9 or the effect of internal waves beneath the sea surface Figure 5.10. (See also Figure 4.26)

The potential for this technique to detect disturbances created by the passage of a submarine seems most promising, if the problem of very large scale data processing of the SAR signal could be solved. Data is produced at the rate of 10^7 numbers per second and very fast computer processors would be needed for real-time ASW. There is still much experimental work to be done.

The greatest surprise, and still not completely understood, was that the SAR images, when tuned to sea surface roughness, revealed a picture of the bottom topography of shallow seas. Figure 5.11 shows the image of the southern sector of the North Sea. The sand banks, and even the sand waves on the banks, were shown in all their fine detail. (The sand waves are of the same type and scale as those in Figure 4.6.) It must be remembered that the features shown on this picture are always covered by water; it is as if the SAR has stripped away the water to reveal the sea bed. The technique seems to be restricted to shallow coastal waters, with strong tides but it promises to be a very useful way of conducting rapid surveys of coastal waters,

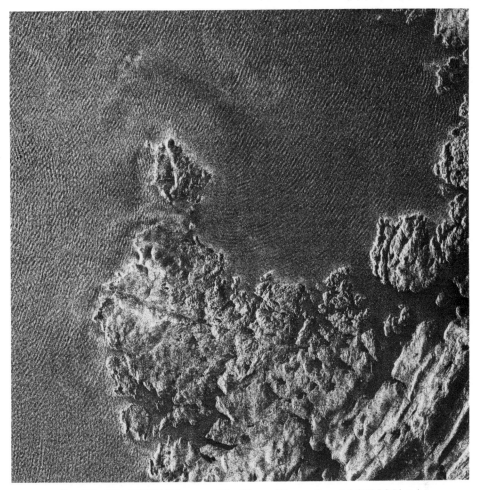

FIG. 5.9   SEASAT SAR Images of Sea Waves (*Crown Copyright/NRSC Photo*)

especially of those areas where there is considerable sand transport, with high, mobile sand waves which could easily interfere with deep-draught shipping.

Ocean Acoustic Tomography

Mesoscale eddies, large internal waves, and isolated movements of large water masses all have effects on ASW. A method of scanning large, deep ocean volumes at little cost would be helpful. Satellites have little use in deep water work, with the possible exception of internal wave propagation.

One step in this direction has been taken with a sonar technique. Arrays of sonar transducers set at various depths and around the perimeter of the water to be studied. Remembering that sound velocity is a function of temperature, salinity and depth, if the array is activated, and signals are processed around all the possible routes, the travel times will indicate the temperature and salinity structure of the water mass; see Figure 5.12. This technique is known as *Ocean Acoustic Tomography*, (after X-ray

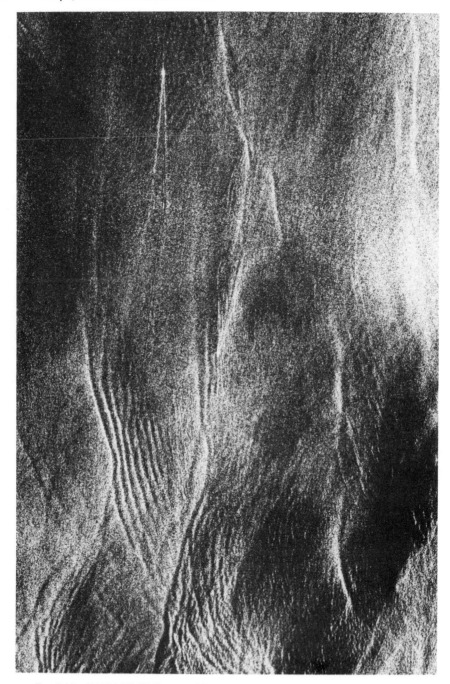

Fɪɢ. 5.10   SEASAT SAR Images of Internal Waves (*Crown Copyright/NRSC Photo*)

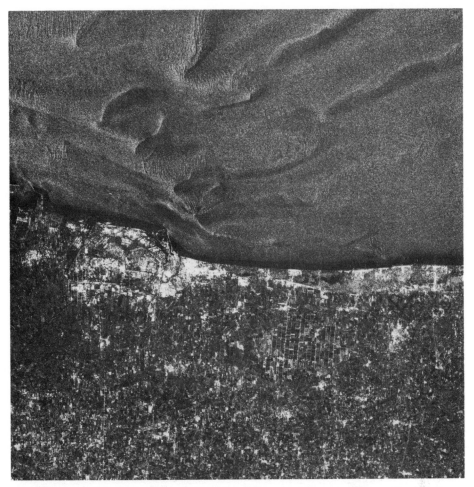

FIG. 5.11   SEASAT SAR Image of the Bottom Topography of the Southern North Sea
(*Crown Copyright/NRSC Photo*)

tomography in medical use) and has been studied over a 300 × 300 kilometre square in the North Atlantic. It might be possible to extend the size of the patient!

Submersibles

The final technique which has made great strides forward since the first beginnings in the 1950s, is the use of the research *submersible*. These are small submarines, with crews of two or three, attended by a mother ship and with a limited endurance. Figure 5.13 shows a typical configuration for the species aimed at the commercial market. These craft have been used in examining the mid-ocean ridge system, for deep-sea biology and numerous other applications including the investigation of old wrecks. Sometimes they have a depth capability which allows work down to the abyssal sea floor; for work in the deep trenches, a very much more specialised

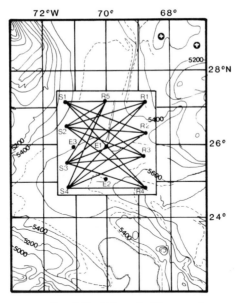

FIG. 5.12   Schematic Diagram of
Ocean Acoustic Tomography

FIG. 5.13   A Typical Commercial Submersible (*Fluid Energy Ltd*)

pressure hull is used. Submersibles find most use, however, in the offshore oil industry, inspecting sea bed pipelines.

Submersibles require complicated life-support systems. It was a logical step forward to develop remote-piloted craft. These are usually attached to the mother ship by an umbilical cord, and an operator in the ship guides the craft using TV cameras. This is a somewhat safer technique than manned craft as, if the device is caught up in an obstruction, it can be abandoned. Limited visibility remains a problem; powerful lamps only illuminate a few square metres of the surrounding water or sea bed. Results must be pieced together from long series of observations.

From the discussion above, oceanographic data collecting has taken great steps forward in the past 15 years. The advance in electronics and the development of reliable instrumentation to install in the corrosive sea water environment has increased knowledge of the behaviour of the deep water, while remote sensing has started to fill some of the mesoscale detail of the surface circulation.

The cost of mounting oceanographic work remains a problem. International co-operation is now the only way of addressing large-scale circulation studies as few countries have the necessary ships and scientists to conduct such experiments on their own. Mathematical modelling of current systems is developing in parallel, straining the resources and capacities of available computers (as mathematical modelling always does!). The prospect of a modelling and predictive system for the circulation of the whole ocean, with mesoscale detail is still to come, but a computer model, fed with real time measurements, much as the international community has with weather forecasting, cannot be too far in the future.

Marine Resources

The oceans have long been a source of resources for mankind. Well known are the offshore rigs, drilling for crude oil and gas in the shallow seas. Well known to the shopper are the fish, *crustaceans*, the hard-shelling marine species, and the 'sea salt' evaporated from the sea water. Perhaps less well known are the other industrial minerals which are extracted from the chemical storehouse of the sea, bromine, iodine and magnesium. For the future, as land-based sources of supply run dry, the oceans will be subjected to increasing investigation, industrialisation and exploitation.

Crude oil and gas lie underneath coastal sea, really by accident in most cases. Continental shelves are part of the adjacent continent, and the reserves are just as likely to lie under dry land. As a result, although they will feature in future naval plans, oil and gas are not 'oceanic' phenomena for consideration here, except to note that exploration is pushing into deeper and deeper water off the edges of the continental shelf, and into Arctic and Antarctic waters. There, they can present the ocean system with a serious pollution problem if a *blowout* occurs and crude oil is allowed to spread into a fragile polar *ecosystem*.

Fish protein is a major industry of all the maritime nations. About 60 per cent of the world catch goes directly for human consumption, the rest is made into animal feedstocks. Managed properly, under international control, fish stocks are a renew-able resource. Estimates of the potential vary, however, from 100 to 2,000 million tonnes per year; exact knowledge is still lacking but an estimate might be four times current catches of around 200 million tonnes. Most of the traditional areas, the northern North Atlantic Ocean for instance, are either fished out, or closely controlled. Modern techniques, such as the CZCS sensor, can detect areas of biological production, and direct fishing fleets from space. (Cosmonauts have been reported advising USSR fishing fleets from SALYUT-6.) Spotter planes are often used to find schools of fish from lower altitudes. Sonar can be tuned to observe fish and steer nets around the school. Freezer trawlers and factory base ships allow fishermen to remain at sea for months. With all this, fish stocks are unlikely to survive without much more study and control of catches; *aquaculture*, the growing of fish under controlled conditions, is being advanced and might be a useful supplement.

Potential still exists in the Indian Ocean and in the Southern Ocean. This latter area, only now being tapped, has an abundance of marine life supported by the *krill*, a small shrimp-like crustacean; while only of use as a source of fish meal, the krill is being looked on as a future crop. The dependence of all the Antarctic species, especially the beleaguered whale, on the krill, means that the problems of fishery control and research in the Southern Ocean needs careful international regulation.

From the water itself, salt—the sodium chloride fraction—bromine and magnesium are currently being extracted. The production of salt, from evaporation in *salt pans*, has been practised since Roman times. Bromine, for use in fuels as an anti-knock agent, is easily extracted chemically from sea water, as is the metal magnesium. Water itself, that is, desalinated water, is also extracted for use in very hot climates.*

Other more exotic chemicals have been looked at. Uranium stocks are not infinite on land and the sea contains 4.4×10^9 tonnes (Table 2.1). Future power requirements might mean tapping this source, as might the extraction of *deuterium*, a heavy *isotope* (or variety) of the gas hydrogen. Deuterium could be used in *fusion* nuclear power reactors, if the technology is ever perfected. The seas hold 200.000 years worth of deuterium.

Mention has already been made of the metalliferous sediments of the rift valleys and the brine pools of the Red Sea. These, and the manganese nodules of the abyssal plains are the major sea bed resources for the future. Again, ownership of these *high seas* assets is debatable, and extraction of commercial quantities, which are at depths of more than 3,000 metres would push current technology to the limits.

The continental shelves, especially those influenced by the last ice age, are an abundant source of sands and gravels. Building projects require more and more of these commodities; in highly-populated areas, Europe for instance, sources of supply on land are drying up and dredging for these aggregates is now a growing industry. Licensing and control of these activities is required, for suitable sandy or pebble beds are usually found to be spawning grounds for fish.

Other *placer* deposits, heavy minerals which were washed off the lands and collected in deeper channels on the continental shelves, continue to be found. Again, the process is associated with the last ice age (see Chapter 1) when these heavy minerals like gold, tin, chromium, titanium and diamonds were emplaced in the river

---

*Proposals were once made for towing Antarctic icebergs from the Southern Oceans to tropical, water-deficient countries. The iceberg would be melted and the fresh water collected and run ashore. Although it might take a year or so to tow a suitable sized berg north, despite the melting *en route*, there would still be a large enough piece left for use.

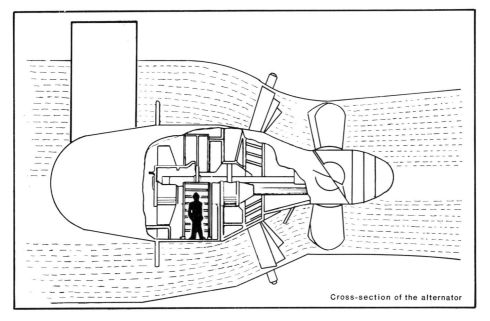

Cross-section of the alternator

Fig. 5.14   The Turbine/Generator Unit of the La Rance Tidal Power Station in France

beds crossing the dry continental shelf. The returning sea and sediments covered the deposits, which are now mined by dredging.

The last item on the list of ocean resources is energy. Three serious sources of energy are being investigated. One is already in use, tidal power.

Tidal power is currently being harnessed successfully in France, Canada and the USSR with other sites with large tidal ranges under active consideration. Figure 5.14 shows the turbine generator used in the La Rance station (550×10^6 kWh of electricity generated per year) in France. The advantages are apparent, the 'fuel' (the rise and fall of the tide) is free. The disadvantage is that there are only two high tides per day and each day their times are one hour later. Such a generating system is hard to link into a national power grid and schemes of energy storage are necessary. Tidal barrages might also cause some environmental problems. They are usually sited on partially-mixed estuaries, see Figure 4.44(b), and the flushing of pollutants out of the river/estuary system is sensitive to such large structures.

Wave power, the extraction of the energy of the wind wave is another possibility. Especially in northern latitudes, there is sufficient energy in the wind waves to power complete countries. The snag is that the energy is offshore and large wave energy generators floating off the coastlines are required. A 500 kilometre array of wave generators, as in Figure 5.15, would be needed to supply the United Kingdom. These units, strung out around the northern coastline, would be a navigational hazard and would modify the coastal environment.

There are several other schemes for wave energy conversion and they might be practical for small isolated communities, as would the '*OTEC*' principle (*Ocean Thermal Energy Conversion*).

This system, Figure 5.16, shows a proposed large-scale device to generate 160,000

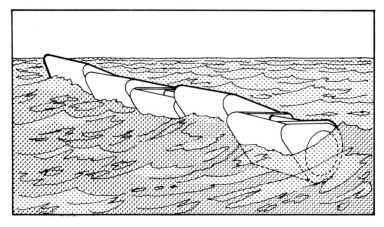

Fig. 5.15   A Salter 'Nodding Duck' Wave Energy Converter

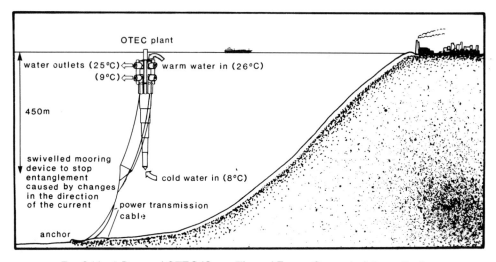

Fig. 5.16   A Proposed OTEC (Ocean Thermal Energy Conversion) Power Station

kilowatts. It uses the warm surface layers and the cold deep water 450 metres below to drive a low boiling-point fluid such as ammonia, and turn a turbine. The principle has been proved and might be applicable to small island communities in tropical climates. An added advantage is that the cold deep water will have a higher nutrient content and this will be pumped to the surface to 'fertilise' the surface layers. The local fishing industry would profit.

All the above schemes are feasible. With conventional energy sources currently inexpensive, the drive to investigate them is limited. The situation might not be the same at the turn of the century.

Marine Pollution

With all the current use, and all the future use proposed above, can the ocean cope? Some rivers are now nothing but open drains, with the sewage and toxic wastes of industry, agriculture and cities. Can the ocean, the ultimate repository of these wastes, retain its health and ecology? Figure 5.17 shows the pathways along which the material travels, from land, to rivers, to estuaries, to coastal seas, to the deep ocean. Table 5.1 catalogues the range of these wastes and their sources.

The list is by no means exhaustive and of course, some items on the list do little damage. Small fish, *fry*, prefer the warm outlet temperatures around power stations. In general, the sea can cope with most of the items; after all, all the 92 elements are

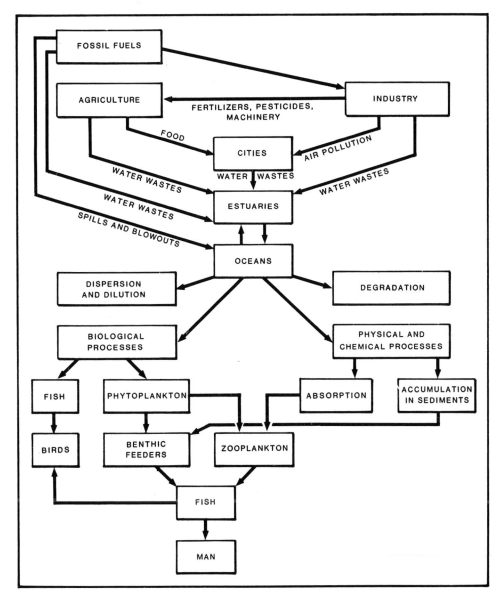

FIG. 5.17   The Cycle of Soluble or Water-Borne Waste Products in the Marine Environment

TABLE 5.1
Wastes Discharged to the Seas and Oceans

Source	Waste Product
Cities	Sewage nutrients Storm drains Oils, street washings
Industry	Chemicals Cooling and process water
Agriculture	Fertilisers Pesticides and herbicides Animal wastes
Power Plants	Coal ash Waste heat Nuclear fuel wastes
Shipping	Waste oil from tanker washings Crude and refined oil from accidents Garbage Sewage Dredging spoils
Oil Exploration	Drilling mud Crude oil spills

already in sea water, albeit in small concentrations, (see Table 2.1) providing the capacity to absorb is not exceeded.*

Before being able to define the capacity of an estuary, coastal sea or ocean, one must know how the material will behave in sea water. Sewage, for instance, in strong tidal currents, with high oxygen levels, rapidly breaks down; the nutrients are returned to the nutrient pool, and in coastal seas, yesterday's supper becomes tomorrow's fish dinner.

Mercury, a relatively harmless element by bacterial action becomes the highly toxic methyl-mercury in coastal rivers and is taken up by the food chain. The inhabitants of the Japanese town of Minimata suffered death and disablement from their fish diet before the culprit was isolated.

To complicate the matter, some organisms concentrate certain elements if they are in excess in the surrounding sea water. For reasons not understood, the oyster, for instance, concentrates zinc and cadmium to levels well above that required for normal metabolism. Zinc is not a problem for human consumption, but cadmium is toxic. Mussels concentrate chromium, lobsters concentrate copper. Sea weed concentrates ruthenium, a rare element only found as a fission product from nuclear reactors and released as a waste product from fuel reprocessing. (In Wales, United Kingdom, sea weeds harvested from near the nuclear fuel reprocessing site in the Irish Sea, used to be made into a food called lava bread.)

*One of the problems in defining the limits is to know the '*background levels*', the amount of any element or compound found naturally. Background or *baseline* studies are needed before defining pollution levels properly. The art of the sea water chemist has not yet been fully developed and, considering the very small concentrations of some elements in sea water, it is no wonder that analytical results have been known to differ from one laboratory to another.

By far the most public pollutant is crude oil. Few years pass without a tanker disaster releasing thousands of tonnes of thick, viscous crude oil on to beaches, killing the wild life. In fact, despite strong international pressure, most crude oil in the ocean comes from the wastes after washing tanks. The *load-on-top* principle of retaining the washings until they can be discharged into onshore tanks has helped; the Mediterranean, which used to suffer severely from this, has improved over the last five years.

The ocean can cope with crude oil. More oil leaks into the sea by natural seepage than is lost by tankers. The sea breaks down the oil and assimilates the by-products back into the food chain. Indeed, the best solution for oil washed ashore on picturesque rocky coasts is to leave it. One or two years of wind and wave will remove the damage and the marine life restores itself. The tourist industry is not keen on this solution, and if the coastline is more fragile, an estuary or mangrove swamp perhaps, the ecological damage is far greater and can persist for tens of years in the sediments.

Tourism itself is a cause of pollution. Concentrations of people along the coasts generate abnormal sewage and garbage loads. The Mediterranean again suffers badly from the pressure of the tourist influx and schemes to provide better sewage processing facilities are being augmented. As more and more people are turning to the coasts, and to boating as a recreation, the sewage pollution levels of some restricted waterways are becoming seriously affected.

Therefore, if any discharge is contemplated, the capacity of the local system must be examined. Long-shore currents, oxygen levels in the water, the proximity of fragile estuarine marsh ecologies or public amenities all need to be taken into consideration. Harbours and docks can no longer absorb untreated sewage and ships in harbours (and even at sea) are processing their own waste before discharge overboard.

Finally, public attitudes to waste dumping have come more to the fore in recent years and look likely to remain a part of any decision-making process. The whale has been saved from extinction by public pressure against the whaling countries, but as yet, it is only the more emotive products, such as nuclear wastes, which receive much attention.

6

Conclusions

In this book we have tried to show that the marine environment is a complex connected system. Whether it is natural or artificial, a disturbance in one part of the system will affect all the rest. Water circulation, for instance, means that pollution caused in one area will, in course of time, spread to many others, possibly causing difficulties for other forms of sea use. Conflicts of interest can therefore easily arise between these different types of sea use, and indeed between countries over their respective shares of the same sea use. Clearly, those responsible for maritime policy need to understand the marine environment system in all its complexity if they are to frame sensible plans of action.

In the last chapter, we touched on another reason why it is so essential for people to understand the marine environment, namely that this complex system is essentially a fragile one. Mankind cannot assume the continued health of the world's oceans; on the contrary this is something which must be actively protected. At a minimum, it is clear that those who use the sea, whether for civil or military purposes, must make sure that they do not do such damage to the environment in which they operate that they must one day face the prospect of its effective loss. Consequently, when designing their equipment, and in utilising it, maritime users must take environmental considerations seriously.

Finally, a knowledge of the behaviour of the ocean continues to be an essential prerequisite for those who would use the sea for military purposes. In days when submarines can hide from their enemies beneath deep scattering layers, behind Gulf Stream fronts and rings or can make use of bottom reverberations, it is obvious that the sailor who 'knows the ground' (to borrow a military expression!) has a tremendous advantage over the one who does not. This requires familiarity not only with the what, but also the why of the marine environment both for fighting men, and for those who design their equipment. This last point is one which will be found to recur constantly in other volumes of this series.

Self Test Questions

Chapter 1

1.1   Using Table 1.2, discuss the reasons for the average salt content of the three oceans.

1.2   Where on the deep ocean sea bed would one most likely find:
    a.   Glacial debris
    b.   Sediments eroded from the land
    c.   Clays weathered from subsurface rocks?

1.3   Using Figure 1.3, identify the major abyssal plains of the World Ocean.

1.4   Using Figure 1.3, identify the major trenches of the oceans.

1.5   Using Figure 1.3, identify the major areas of continental shelf.

1.6   Using Figure 1.3, identify the major coastal seas. Classify them as 'continental shelf seas' or 'deep ocean seas'.

1.7   Briefly describe the bottom topography of the Arctic Ocean.

1.8   Using Figure 1.7, identify those oceans which are expanding or contracting.

1.9   Using Figure 1.3, identify the major groups of oceanic islands and suggest whether they are the result of hot spot activity.

1.10   Sediments are washed off the world land mass into the oceans at the rate of 9.6 $\times 10^9 m^3\ yr^{-1}$. If the oceans have existed for at least 4×10^9 years what problem do these figures and the data in Table 1.1 suggest?

Chapter 2

2.1   Briefly explain why water is such a good solvent.

2.2   What are the reasons for the Plimsoll Line on the side of a ship? Why are different levels marked for different climates and types of water?

2.3   The stability of a ship results from the production of a righting moment, GZ, as the ship heels. Explain the physical process which results in GZ and indicate the key features of the curve of GZ against the angle of heel.

2.4   What are the consequences of flooding? How can these effects be ameliorated and what are the consequent penalties of the measures taken?

2.5   Explain the means by which a submarine dives, maintains depth and subsequently resurfaces.

2.6   Explain the mechanisms which cause steel to rust. Why does stainless steel not exhibit the same propensity to rust?

2.7   Describe the active and passive measures for the protection of the hull against corrosion.

Chapter 3

3.1   Name the six climatic winds and describe the mechanisms which produce them. Where do perturbations to these winds (depressions and anticyclones) occur?

3.2   Explain the difference between wave speed and group speed. Show that the group speed of two Gerstner waves which combine is half the wave speed of the individual waves.

3.3   Draw a trochoidal wave form of wave length 15.7 centimetres and height 2 centimetres.

3.4   Explain the term *significant wave height* and give the significant wave height for each Sea State number. What wind speeds are associated with each Sea State, and under what conditions would the Sea State *not* result from such wind speeds.

3.5   What are the consequences of *flexure*? How does this differ from *working*?

3.6   Explain why both the *encounter spectrum* and the *Response Amplitude Operator* are required to predict a ship's motion.

3.7   What are the operational penalties caused by ship's motion in a sea-way? How could a hull be changed to improve operational performance in high sea states?

3.8   Which active stabilisation system would be most appropriate for (a) a minehunter during slow speed operations, and (b) an escort vessel?

3.9   A short beamy ship has a natural roll period of 0.25 s, whereas a longer, narrower ship of the same displacement has a period of 0.5 s. Which would roll more when experiencing the mixed swell and sea spectrum, Figure 3.18? Even if roll amplitude were equal, which ship's complement would suffer less from the effects of sea sickness?

3.10   Consider how the accretion of ice would affect the *GZ* curve and explain why de-icing would be important.

Chapter 4

4.1   Describe the features seen in the nine profiles of Figure 4.1.

4.2   Name all the major ocean surface currents from Figure 4.6.

4.3   What will be the period of an inertial current at latitude 52°N?

4.4   What is the evidence for the motion of the waters in the deep ocean?

4.5   If a water mass 'A', with temperature 4.0°C and salinity 34.8, is mixed with water mass 'B' of temperature 9°C and salinity 35.5, in the ratio 10:1, what will the resulting water mass 'C' have as its temperature and salinity?

4.6   Briefly describe how a parcel of water might leave the Norwegian Sea and travel to the Mid-Pacific Ocean following a deep water route.

4.7   What would be the velocity of an internal wave propagating on a density interface between an upper water layer of 100 metres thickness, density $1.025 \times 10^3 \, kg \, m^{-3}$, and a lower layer of 2,000 metres thickness and density $1.0275 \times 10^3 \, kg \, m^{-3}$?

4.8   What bottom sediments would one expect under zones of *upwelling*? (See Question 2, Chapter 1.)

4.9   Briefly explain what is meant by the *Equilibrium Tide*

4.10   Calculate the velocity of a tsunami of wave length 100 kilometres travelling across an ocean 4,000 metres deep.

4.11   Explain the difference between the circulation in a salt-wedge and a partially-mixed estuary. What effect do rivers have on the circulation of the adjacent coastal sea?

4.12   What is the difference between spherical and cylindrical spreading losses of a sonar signal?

4.13   Describe the effect of the *Deep Scattering Layer* on the propagation of a sonar signal.

4.14   Trace the path of sonar signals trapped in the *surface duct*.

4.15   Trace the path of sonar signals trapped in the *SOFAR Channel*.

4.16   Explain the importance of *fronts* in anti-submarine warfare.

Chapter 5

5.1   List oceanic phenomena which are most usefully studied with *synoptic* observations.

5.2   Describe what is meant by *Eulerian* and *Lagrangian* methods of measuring currents in the ocean.

5.3 Briefly   discuss   the   various   types   of   space-borne   oceanographic instrumentation.

5.4   List all those aspects of the oceans which have a bearing on a nation's maritime commitment, for instance: fish stocks and fishery protection.

Further Reading

1. Oceanography Series. Pergamon Press set (1989) consisting of the following volumes:
   a. The Ocean Basins: Their Structure and Evolution.
   b. Sea Water: Its Composition, Properties and Behaviour.
   c. Ocean Circulation.
   d. Ocean Chemistry and Deep Sea Sediments.
   e. Waves, Tides and Shallow Water Processes.
   f. Case Studies in Oceanography and Marine Affairs.

An excellent general set of text books (excluding marine biology) on all aspects of oceanography, for a third year university course (S330) written by a group from The Open University.
Some titles in the set have not been published.

2. An Introduction to Marine Ecology (2nd edn.), Barnes, R. S. K., and Hughes, R. N., Blackwell Scientific Publications, 1988.

   The textbook used by the Open University to complete the third year course on oceanography and fill the gap on marine biology and ecology.

3. Descriptive Regional Oceanography, Tchernia, P., Pergamon Press Marine Series, vol. 3, 1980.

   A good text describing the water masses and circulation of the oceans and seas.

4. Environmental Oceanography: An Introduction to the Behaviour of Coastal Waters, Beer, T., Pergamon Press, 1983.

   A short, useful text covering all aspects of coastal oceanography with chapters on pollution, remote sensing, modelling and assessment.

5. The Oceans—Their Physics, Chemistry and General Biology, Sverdrup, H. U., Johnson, M. W., and Fleming, R. H., Prentice-Hall, 1942.

   A monumental book covering the science of oceanography as known in the 1940s. Although dated, it is still a valuable reference text.

6. Basic Ship Theory (3rd edn.), 2 vols., Rawson, K. J., and Tupper, E. C., Longman, 1983.

   The standard undergraduate text for naval architects.

171

7. Submarine Design and Development, Friedman, N., Conway Maritime Press, 1984.

   An excellent descriptive text covering submarine design and development, profusely illustrated.

8. Corrosion—Causes and Prevention, Laque, F. L., Wiley, 1975.

   A good discussion on the corrosion of materials in sea water.

9. Wind Waves—Their Generation and Propagation on the Ocean Surface, Kinsman, B., Prentice-Hall, 1965.

   Still the standard undergraduate text on wind waves.

10. Ocean Wave Statistics, Hogben, N., and Lumb, R. F., HMSO, 1967.

11. Global Wave Statistics, British Maritime Technology, 1986.

12. Designing Ships to the Natural Environment, Bales, S. L., *Naval Engineers' Journal*, vol. 95, pp. 31–40, 1983.

13. Motion Sickness Incidence: Exploratory Studies of Habitation, McCauley, M. E. et al., Human Factors Research Inc., 1976.

14. Principles of Underwater Sound (3rd edn.), Urick, R. J., McGraw-Hill, 1983.

   A standard reference for the behaviour of sound in the sea and the principles of propagation and detection.

15. Manual of Seamanship, 3 vols., HMSO, 1981.

16. Satellite Oceanography—An Introduction for Oceanographers and Remote Sensing Scientists, Robinson, I. S., Ellis Horwood, 1985.

   A complete review of modern space-borne instrumentation for oceanography.

17. Oceanography and Seamanship, Van Doren, W. G., Granada Publishing, 1974.

   A well-written discussion on oceanography as it affects the mariner.

18. Fundamentals of Naval Surface Ship Weight Estimating, Stroubinger, E. K., Curren, W. C. and Fighern, V. L., *Naval Engineers' Journal*, vol. 95, pp. 127–143, 1983.

19. Design of Ship Superstructures in Fibre-reinforced Plastic, Smith, C. S., and Chalmers, D. W., Trans. RINA, 1986.

20. Introductory Dynamic Oceanography, Pond, S., and Pickard, G. L., Pergamon Press, 1978.

   A good introduction to the mathematics of currents, waves and ocean circulation.

Index